D1483804

ORGANIC
SEMICONDUCTORS

Yoshiyuki

Y. OKAMOTO

and

WALTER BRENNER

Research Division
School of Engineering and Science
New York University

New York
REINHOLD PUBLISHING CORPORATION
Chapman & Hall, Ltd., London

Preface

The remarkable growth of interest in the physics and chemistry of the organic solid state is reflected by a steady increase in the number of published investigations dealing with various aspects of this subject. Research on the organic solid state is increasingly being recognized as an interdisciplinary field of study which combines related work not only by chemists and physicists but also by electrical engineers, biologists and even medical researchers. While some of the initial impetus for such research has no doubt been stimulated by the progress which has been achieved from the study of the solid state properties of inorganic materials, particularly as related to semiconductivity phenomena and their practical utilization, organic solid state science has now made enough strides to stand on its own feet, so to speak. The theoretical and practical consequences of studies of the organic solid state can as yet not be clearly ascertained, and they may not necessarily follow the route set by the inorganics. It is proper to expect however that a better understanding of the organic solid state will give us, at the very least, increased insight not only into the electronic properties of organic solids but also into energy conversion systems, luminescence and even certain biological processes.

The rather diffuse nature of this very broad subject has prompted the publication of pertinent investigations in a great number of different journals not all of which are those routinely perused by chemists and physicists. This has made it difficult for the individual researcher interested in this field to maintain adequate contact with all of the important developments. Because of this, the authors have decided to offer the subsequent survey of organic semiconductors which, it is hoped, will tie together much diverse and apparently unrelated work into some sort of order and coherence. This present book should then be considered as a progress report rather than a definitive treatise—a progress report reflecting recent research and its difficulties in an admittedly very complex field. Because of the authors' background, the point of view taken throughout has been that of the chemist rather than the physicist. Photoconductivity, an admittedly very important subject related to the study of the organic solid state, has not been discussed, both on account of its far reaching implications which encompass such matters as photosynthesis and for reasons of space; it is felt that photoconductivity well deserves a separate study. This book, therefore, is centered on an account of research on the dark conductivity characteristics of organic solids and their manifold effects on the properties of organic materials.

It has obviously been impossible to review and give credit to every reported investigation; much effort has been exercised however to include all of the important references up to early 1963. Because of the fast-moving nature of this field, however, certain specific important work may not have been credited; in all such cases the authors acknowledge their fault and ask for understanding.

As with any work of this type, the authors would like to acknowledge the cooperation and help of the many individuals without whom this book could not have been completed; it is a special pleasure to thank Dr. A. F. Armington, U.S. Air Force Cambridge Research Laboratories, who prepared the chapter on the Electronic Properties of Carbons, Drs. M. Pope and Y. Matsunaga who commented on sections of the book; Dr. M. Sano who read this book in its entirety and made valuable suggestions; and Mrs. A. Gordon who performed the formidable task of preparing the entire manuscript.

University Heights
Bronx, New York
August, 1964

Y. OKAMOTO
WALTER BRENNER

Contents

1

Introduction

The vast number of chemicals which are conventionally classified within the province of organic chemistry are generally considered in terms of electrical insulators. In recent years, however, an increasing number of organic compounds has been discovered to exhibit pertinent electrical characteristics which do not fit this concept.[1,2] The term "organic semiconductors" has been used to describe organic solids which contain a significant amount of carbon-to-carbon bonding but show some capability of supporting electronic conduction.[3,4] A common factor in all definitions is the employment of the property of electrical resistivity as a distinguishing material characteristic. It is customary to consider organic semiconductors as materials which exhibit electronic conductivities in between those of metals (10^4 to 10^6 ohm^{-1} cm^{-1}) and insulators (10^{-22} to 10^{-10} ohm^{-1} cm^{-1}), that is the broad range of 10^{-9} to 10^{+3} ohm^{-1} cm^{-1}.

Semiconducting organic solid materials are frequently grouped into the categories of molecular crystals, charge transfer complexes, and polymers. Molecular crystals such as naphthalene and anthracene are among the most thoroughly studied organic compounds. Very low resistivities have been measured on diverse charge transfer complexes, the further investigation of which may have important implications for biological systems. Polymers including the so-called pyropolymers are being extensively investigated with emphasis on conjugated long chain structures. The primary aim of current research is to obtain a better understanding of the mechanisms of electron transfer in molecular solids and the relation of such mechanisms to the physicochemical structures of such solids. Research in organic semiconductors is carried out mainly at the basic level but has created much interest in various industrial organizations, particularly those interested in solid state properties.

Historically the study of the electronic conductivity of organic solid compounds may be traced back to the beginning of this century. The discovery of the photoconduction of solid anthracene was described by Pochettino in 1906.[5] Koenigsberger and Schilling demonstrated the existence of a small but measurable dark conduction in anthracene.[6] A number of additional papers was published, but by 1914 interest in this field had almost completely lapsed—a situation which was to prevail for almost twenty years.

Some experiments were carried out in subsequent years on the problem of photoconduction in certain organic dystuffs. Vartanyan was particularly interested in the part which photoconduction plays in the sensitization of photographic emulsions and published extensively in this area.[7,8,9] Electronic excitation of the dystuff molecules followed by transfer of an electron to the silver halide was considered to be an important step of the sensitization process. A recent review of this field has been published.[10]

Szent-Györgyi is generally credited with having helped to revive the study of organic semiconductors by publications in 1941 in which he suggested that the transfer of π electrons from molecule to molecule may play an important role in the fundamental processes of biological systems.[11,12] Photoconduction of certain dyed proteins was reported by Szent-Györgyi in 1946 as evidence for the validity of his original proposition.[13] The significant revival of interest in organic semiconductors is reflected by a steadily increasing number of papers on the subject of conduction and photoconduction in organic materials in subsequent years. Of special interest is the discovery in 1948 by Eley of the exponential variation of the conductivity of certain phthalocyanines with the reciprocal of the temperature, which relationship was later found to be equally applicable to various other organic compounds.[14] Photosynthesis was related to organic semiconductivity by Katz,[15] Bradley,[16] and

Calvin.[17] Semiconductivity has been connected to carcinogenesis by Pullman and others.[18,19]

The demonstration of the remarkably low conductivities which are exhibited by certain charge transfer complexes, as shown by Akamatu, Inokuchi, and Matsunaga in 1954, marked yet another milestone in the study of organic semiconductors.[20,21] Many other charge transfer complexes have since then been shown to possess semiconductive behavior.[1,2] Polymeric phthalocyonines have been studied by Wildi and Epstein.[22] Recent reviews have indicated the major types of organic polymeric semiconductors studied to date.[23,24,25] Research in organic semiconductors is now proceeding at a much faster pace stimulated in no small measure by the remarkable technological progress which was achieved with silicon, germanium, and other inorganic semiconductors.

It has been noted above that the major aim of current investigations is the better understanding of the nature of the electron transport processes in molecular solids especially as related to their physicochemical structure. There exists, however, an exciting practical potential as well. The organic chemist having at his disposal over 900,000 different organic compounds and considerable synthetic skills may be able to tailor make semiconductor materials with properties exactly matched to the requirements of specific applications. Thus, fabricators of electronic devices can conceive of completely new films, filaments and molded shapes specially prepared to best suit particular purposes. Furthermore such novel products have the additional promise of lower materials costs and more ready fabricability compared to inorganic semiconductors. While it is too early to attempt to predict the future development of this exiting new discipline, the rapid progress which is being made now augurs well for the future. There is considerable basis for the confidence of the chemical industry to be able to convert the basic research results now being developed, into useful industrial products in application potentials ranging from thermoelectricity to sea water desalination. When the character of electronic conductivity in molecular solids is better understood, basic life processes such as photosynthesis and cell conditions may also be better explainable and, hence, controllable.

The accomplishment of these tasks is a large order indeed. The

4   ORGANIC SEMICONDUCTORS

combined efforts of the organic, physical, and polymer chemists, as well as of physicists, mathematicians, and medical researchers, will be necessary to arrive at satisfactory solutions. It is certain that, regardless of what will be learned about organic semiconductivity in the laboratory, new and important developments in almost any area of knowledge will spring from such basic studies. It is this belief which has made this field so attractive to both science and industry.

References

1. Garrett, C. G. B., "Organic Semiconductors" (Chapter XV) in "Semiconductors," Ed. by N. B. Hannay, New York, Reinhold Publishing Corp., 1960.
2. Inokuchi, H., and Akamatu, H., "Electrical Conductivity of Organic Semiconductors" in "Solid State Physics," Ed., F. Seitz and D. Turnbull, New York, Academic Press, 1961.
3. Brophy, J. J., *Physics Today*, **14**, No. 8, 40 (1961).
4. Brophy, J. J., and Buttrey, J. W., "Organic Semiconductors," Proceedings of as Inter Industry Conference, Chicago, New York, Macmillan Co., April, 1961.
5. Pochettino, A., *Acad. Lincei Rendic.*, **15**, 355 (1906).
6. Koenigsberger, J., and Schilling, K., *Ann. Physik.* **32**, 179 (1910).
7. Vartanyan, A. T., *Actre Physiochim URSS*, **22**, 201 (1947).
8. Vartanyan, A. T., *Zhur. Fiz. Khim.*, **22**, 769 (1948).
9. Vartanyan, A. T., *Doklady Akad. Nauk SSSR*, **71**, 641 (1950).
10. Mitchell, J. W., *Rep. Prog. in Phys.*, **20**, 433 (1957).
11. Szent-Györgyi, A., *Science*, **93**, 609 (1941).
12. Szent-Györgyi, A., *Nature*, **148**, 157 (1941).
13. Szent-Györgyi, A., *Nature*, **157**, 875 (1946).
14. Eley, D. D., *Nature*, **162**, 189 (1948).
15. Katz, E., in "Photosynthesis in Plants," p. 291, Iowa State Press, 1949.
16. Bradley, D. F., and Calvin, M., *Proc. Natl. Acad. Sc. U.S.*, **41**, 563 (1955).
17. Calvin, M., *Rev. Mod. Phys.*, **31**, 147, 157 (1959).
18. Pullman, A., and Pullman, B., *Advances in Cancer Research*, **3**, 117 (1955).
19. Mason, R., *Disc. Faraday Soc.*, **27**, 129 (1959).
20. Akamatu, H., Inokuchi, H., and Matsunaga, Y., *Bull. Chem. Soc. Japan*, **29**, 213 (1956).
21. Akamatu, H., Inokuchi, H., and Matsunaga, Y., *Nature*, **173**, 168 (1954).
22. Epstein, A., and Wildi, B. S., *J. Chem. Phys.*, **33**, 324 (1960).
23. Atlas, S. M., Becker, M., and Mark, H. F., *SPE Transact.*, 169 (Oct. 1961).
24. Hatano, H., "Synthesis of Polyorganic Semiconductor," *Yukigosei Kagaku Kiyokaishi (Japan)*, **20**, 326 (1962).
25. Pohl, H. A., "Semiconduction in Polymers" in "Organic Semiconductors," Ed. by J. J. Brophy and J. W. B. Buttrey, New York, Macmillan Co., 1961.

2

Electronic Conduction Mechanism
in Organic Materials

The spectacular advances which have been made in the theory, preparation, and applications of inorganic semiconductors, such as silicon and germanium, have no doubt accelerated analogous investigations of the conduction mechanism in organic materials. Investigations of organic semiconductors have tended to confirm the existence of such compounds and increasingly emphasize the close relationship between the physics and chemistry of semiconductors. Thus, a full understanding of either area can be gained only by considering the relation between them. Today it is already possible to prepare organic solids with a very wide range of electronic properties, although an adequate understanding of the mechanisms of conduction is still lacking. It is the purpose of this chapter to describe some of the theoretical concepts which have been advanced for a better understanding of the many and often isolated experimental facts observed to date.

From a chemical point of view the better organic conductors have been classified as compounds which have a number of delocalized electrons (π electrons) in the molecules, free radicals, and charge transfer complexes. Although considerable experimental work has been carried out on the preparation and the study of the electronic properties of these materials, no comprehensive theory of the conduction mechanism in organic solids has as yet been proposed. A principal reason for this state of affairs is the fragmentary and generally less than satisfactory knowledge of intermolecular interactions in the solid state.

The most widely used explanation of the experimentally observed conduction phenomenae of organic solids is in terms of a modified electronic band model of these solids. This is essentially a quantum mechanical approach involving the calculation of the width of energy bands by calculating overlap integrals between π electron molecular wave functions on adjacent molecules. The relative weakness of the intermolecular attractions in molecular crystals results in rather narrow conduction bands and low carrier mobilities. A summary of this approach which, while admittedly imperfect, may help in the analysis and evaluation of experimental data follows.

When the temperature of organic crystals is increased to a suitable degree, thermal excitation will occasionally raise an electron from the ground state to the excited conducting state. Thus, a "hole" is created as well as a conduction electron. The processes of thermal excitation and recombination of electrons and holes continue until a dynamic equilibrium is established. This state is characterized by a time independent electrical conductivity. By raising the solid to a sufficiently high temperature, any insulator can be expected to show this type of behavior, which has been called "intrinsic" semiconduction since it is an intrinsic property of the material. The process corresponds to a thermal excitation across the forbidden gap, from the valence band to the conduction band. The temperature necessary to develop intrinsic semiconduction is a function of the width of the forbidden energy gap (Figure 2-1).

For materials containing impurities, the electronic conductivity may be controlled by the impurities. Such behavior is called "extrinsic" semiconduction, as it depends on the nature of the impurities and the concentration of imperfections in the crystal lattice. However, very little is known about the role of impurities in the organic semiconductors.

For inorganic semiconductors, boron in germanium offers an example of an extrinsic semiconductor in which an excess of holes has been introduced. Semiconductors which have an excess of holes over conduction electrons are called "p-type," because their conductivity arises from the presence of positive current carriers.

Those with an excess of electrons are called "n-type" since the carriers are negative. The current carriers are called majority or minority carriers depending on which predominate. A semiconductor in its intrinsic range has equal concentrations of holes and electrons, as discussed above.

When the energy gap is expressed by ϵ, the concentration of the current carriers (holes and electrons) should then vary with temperature according to the following relationship:

$$n = n_0 \exp\left(-\epsilon/2kT\right) \tag{1}$$

where k is Boltzmann's constant and n_0 is a constant. ϵ is the difference in energy between the highest point in the valence band and

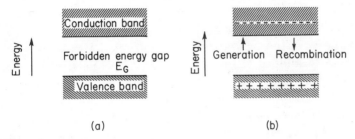

Figure 2-1. Intrinsic semiconductor, (a.) at low temperature, (b.) at elevated temperature, with thermal excitation generating holes and conduction electrons.

the lowest point in the conduction band. The factor of $\frac{1}{2}$ in the exponent appears with intrinsic semiconductors because the possible distributions of electrons in the conduction band are independent of the distributions of holes in the valence band. Then, the conductivity may generally be expressed as follows:

$$\sigma = |e|(n_n\mu_n + n_p\mu_p) \tag{2}$$

where n_n is the density of electrons, n_p is the density of positive holes, μ_n and μ_p are the mobility for electron and hole.

If it is assumed that the mobility of the carrier varies rather slowly with temperature,[1] Equation (1) may be then rewritten for the experimental conductivity as follows:

$$\sigma = |e|(\mu_n + \mu_p)n_0 \exp\left(-E/kT\right) \tag{3}$$

and

$$\sigma = \sigma_0 \exp\left(-E/kT\right) \qquad (4)$$

where σ_0 is a constant and $E = \frac{1}{2}\epsilon$. In this equation the energy term is one of the most important factors for the study of organic semiconductors.

A number of authors assume that the dark conductivity of organic crystals is indeed conventional intrinsic semiconductivity, and they use ϵ as the band gap of such crystals. The observed values of ϵ and E_t are almost equal leading to the further assumption that the molecular triplet state is involved in the conduction.[2] However, the validity of this assumption was criticized by Fox who advocates the following point of view.[3,4]

He considers that, in organic crystals, the overlaps of the molecular orbitals are generally very small. It would, therefore, be reasonable that the orbitals of one molecule be isolated from that of others. Because of their isolation, any free electron formed may spend most of the time in the neighborhood of one molecule or another and very little time in the interstitial regions. A similar consideration applies also to free holes states. The carriers (electron or hole) which spend a long time at some molecule will jump to a neighbor's molecule by the perturbations arising from the presence of other molecules (hopping model).

Examples of such conduction mechanisms can be found in inorganic semiconductors such as NiO and Fe_2O_3. In NiO, for example, the overlaps of the $3d$ orbital in Ni^{++} are very small; and the $3d$ band in Ni is only $\frac{1}{15}$ as wide as the $4s$ band. The narrowness of the band implies a high effective mass and low carrier mobility in the band. The mobility at $300°K$ is 0.004 cm^2/V-sec and increases exponentially with temperature, with an activation energy of 0.1 eV. Conduction in NiO and Fe_2O_3 by the above mechanism presumes that a potential barrier exists which must be overcome to enable a charge carrier to jump from one location to another.[5]

To find the excitation energy for the lowest conducting state for the hopping model or the band model,[6] the charge transfer mechanism is considered to occur in several steps. The electron is first removed from its original molecular location to a point far from the crystal; this requires the ionization energy E_I. Bringing the electron back to the crystal and placing it on the second molecule involves the electron affinity energy E_A. If the ion pair is widely separated, each ion will polarize the surrounding molecules. The energy, W, of interaction of each ion with the polarization is identical for the two ions, as a first approximation. The excitation energy is then $E_I - E_A - 2W$. There are other considerations, but they are small in effect compared with those considered above.

Either the electrons on the negative ions or the hole left behind on the positive ions can carry current by hopping to adjacent molecules. The two charges are sufficiently far apart that they act independently of one another.

The applicability of either the band model or the hopping model concepts for an explanation of the conduction mechanism of organic crystals can, in some cases, be evaluated by measurements of the temperature dependence of the carrier mobility.

If the mobility is of a higher than 1 cm²/V-sec, the carriers are considered to be moving about freely within a band and are periodically scattered by collision with phonons in crystals. The mobility increases with decreasing temperatures because of a decrease in the number of phonons or scattering centers. However, if the mobility is less than 1 cm²/V-sec, it seems more reasonable to consider the localization of the charge carriers on particular lattice sites. Recently Kepler has reported on mobility measurements in athracene.[7] He found that the mobilities were in the order of 1 cm²/V-sec and also that they are anisotrophic (see Chapter 3). The calculated values by LeBlanc are in quite good agreement with these experimental data.[8,9]

Thus, the transport mechanism of holes and electrons in anthracene can be described with a band model. However, the band model need not be necessarily applicable to other systems, particularly so if the following anthracene experimental restrictions are obviated:[9]

(a) the material under study exhibits a periodic lattice;

(b) the carrier concentrations are so small that carrier interactions can be considered negligible.

In liquid hexane the mobilities of photoelectrically injected electrons are quite small (10^{-3} cm²/V-sec) and exhibit the Arrhenius temperature dependence.[10] The mechanism of transport is not yet clear, but one possibility is that, upon melting, a band model mechanism may be replaced by a hopping model mechanism. This may also be true in amorphous polymeric materials.

The increased number of investigations dealing with the phenomena of electronic conductivity in organic solids offers a real hope for adding substantially to our understanding of the more relevant parameters pertaining to the conduction mechanism. However, much more experimental work is indicated on such problems as measurement of material purities, determination of carrier types and mobilities, ionization energy values, and electrode and temperature effects for various materials of interest.

References

1. Dexter, D. H., and Seitz, F., *Phys. Rev.*, **86,** 964 (1952).
2. Carswell, D. J., Ferguson, J., and Lyons, L. E., *Nature*, **173,** 736 (1954).
3. Fox, D., "Electrical Conductivity in Organic Solids," Ed. by H. Kallmann and M. Silver, p. 239. New York, Interscience Publishers, 1960.
4. Fox, D., *J. Phys. Chem. Solids*, **8,** 439 (1959).
5. Morin, F. J., "Semiconductors," Ed. by N. B. Hannay, p. 600, New York, Reinhold Publishing Corp.; 1959.
6. Lyons, L. E., *J. Chem. Soc.*, 5001 (1957).
7. Kepler, R. G., *Phys. Rev.*, **119,** 1226 (1960).
8. LeBlanc, O. H., Jr., *J. Chem. Phys.*, **35,** 1275 (1961).
9. LeBlanc, O. H., Jr., "Organic Semiconductors," Ed. by J. J. Brophy and J. W. Buttrey, p. 21, New York, The MacMillan Co., 1962.
10. LeBlanc, O. H., Jr., *J. Chem. Phys.*, **30,** 1443 (1959).

3

Measurement Techniques

The design and execution of measurement techniques capable of the reproducible and accurate determination of the electronic properties of organic solids is being increasingly appreciated as a most important and necessary task for the orderly development of the field of organic semiconductors. In the past, the use of conductivity measurements to characterize the charge density and/or mobility parameters of organic solids has been attempted by various investigators. Most materials have been measured in the forms of compressed bulk specimen although thin film specimen and rather recently single-crystal specimen have also been investigated. A number of conductivity cells with different designs have been employed to carry out such measurements. There exist, however, significant differences in the quantitative data obtained on the same compound as measured by various investigators. The electrical conductivity of most materials is apparently a function of many, otherwise minor variables such as impurity content, environment, pressure on sample, surface effects, and degree of crystallinity. Considering, the many variables involved the most useful measurements have been made on large crystals of high purity inorganic materials such as silicon and germanium.

Relatively little is known about the measurement of Hall effects and other significant parameters for the further characterization of organic semiconductors. Such information will undoubtedly develop as the field progresses. It is the purpose of this discussion to describe the current and frequently unsatisfactory state of progress in this most important area of the organic semiconductor field.

Techniques for the Measurement of Electrical Resistivity

Conductivity data of organic semiconductors have frequently been obtained by measuring the d-c resistance of compressed powder samples. This procedure assumes the elimination of interparticle contact resistance due to the pressure application. Other measurements have been performed by fusing such powders under pressure into hard, brittle pellets which were then shaped into pellets suitable for four probe measurements. It has recently been pointed out that while such measurement methods can yield qualitatively interesting information, they are of limited utility for theoretical interpretations because they mask such important phenomena as crystallite anisotropy, interparticle contact resistance, and surface effects.[1]

In an attempt to eliminate the interparticle contact resistances, a-c methods of resistance measurements have been used by many workers.. The technique consists of determining the net effective resistance of a sample at audio or radio frequencies using suitable bridge or Q meters.[2,3,4] This is based on the somewhat doubtful assumption that at sufficiently high frequencies the high resistance contact is electrically shorted by its own capacitance with the remaining resistance being related to the bulk resistivity of the particles themselves.[1]

The electrical resistivity of a material has been defined as the ratio of the current density to the applied field. The conventional measuring technique consists of applying a known voltage across a sample of known dimensions and determining the current in the external current. Two possible major problems can arise with this technique of measuring electrical resistivity. First of all the contact at the electrode—sample interface may have such a high resistance that it can effect a significant voltage drop across the electrode rather than the sample. Also there is the possibility of the injection of electron hole carriers into what would otherwise be an insulator by the act of the placement of metal electrodes on the surface.

It must be pointed out that considerable advances have been

made in the measurement of very high resistances such as plastic insulators. Several decades ago, 10^9 ohms was considered to be an indefinite resistance. However, recent methods permit the measurement of resistances of 10^{20} to 10^{22} ohms.[5] One such method is based on the use of a voltage divider integrating in conjunction with commercially available high impact impedance electrometers. These improved techniques permit the characterization of high quality dielectrics and offer the possibility of the accurate measurement and suitable differentiation of organic solid compounds with high but different resistivities.

The absence of suitable quality crystals of organic solids has made necessary the use of other kinds of test specimen and measurement methods. The three most usual approaches have been d-c measurements on compressed powder, four probes,[6] d-c measurements on mechanically fused samples and various a-c techniques on powders. The most usual measurement technique employed in the past was the determination of the resistance of a compressed disc between metal electrodes, frequently under pressure. Various electrode materials have been used satisfactorily including gold, silver, mercury, and platinum. Tests have also been carried out to ascertain the effect of the amount of applied pressure on the resistivity of the test specimen (see page 32, Effect of Pressures). A limiting resistance has been defined in terms of that resistance value where further pressure application does not cause significantly additional reduction of the measured resistance value. It is assumed that with pressure applications in excess of this limiting pressure, the interparticle contact resistance problem has been effectively minimized or eliminated.

A fairly large number of data have been obtained with a considerable variety of compressed powder bulk specimen of organic semiconductors which indicates that the resistivity becomes a practically constant value when such specimens are subjected to pressures in excess of 80 to 100 kg/cm^2.[7] A typical example of this relationship is shown in Figure 3-1.

The Preparation of Conductivity Cells

Powder Specimen. Although the art of preparing large crystals has been substantially advanced in the past decade, the organic materials of interest for semiconductor studies are generally available only in the form of powders comprising minute crystals or amorphous materials with limited crystallinity. Single crystals are rather difficult to obtain and generally require lengthy and exacting preparative procedures. They are available only for a limited number of compounds.. The types of conductivity cells which have been employed for the measurement of the electrical resistivity of organic semiconductor materials in powder form are described below.

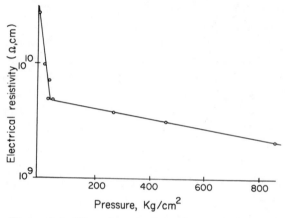

Figure 3-1. The pressure dependence of the resistivity of isoviolanthrone at 65°C.

An early arrangement consists of packing the powder specimen into a wall insulated cylinder, e.g., ebonite or quartz cylinder, and compressing it between the electrodes. In one version a lever system was designed to effect the powder compression. This type of conductivity cell was employed for the measurement of the electrical resistivity of powdered graphite.

Akamatu and Inokuchi have refined this apparatus by control of temperature, etc. This was done by heating the specimen from the outside with a small electrical oven. The inside surface of the oven was copper plate which was then neutralized to prevent any electrical disturbance. Applied pressures up to 300 kg/cm² were used. Specimen thickness ranged from 0.1 to 4.3 cm.

A somewhat different conductivity cell is depicted in Figure 3-2. Here the specimen is compressed onto a cylindrical dish made of brass coated with chromium, by means of a piston furnishing pressures up to 80 kg/cm². The piston is insulated by four sleeves of ambroides and a "Pyrex" rod. This type of cell is said to be suitable for the measurements of compounds with rather high resistivities as it is free from the material of specimen container. Eley and his collaborators prepared conductivity cells by placing compressed

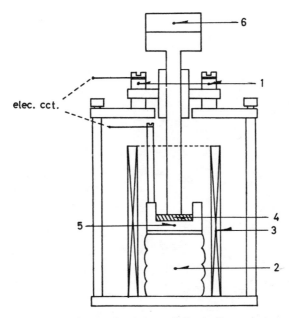

Figure 3-2. The conductivity cell for bulk specimens:
1. sleeve of ambroide, 2. "Pyrex" rod, 3. electrical
oven, 4. specimen, 5. cylindrical dish, and 6. weight.

powder discs between noble metal electrodes and carried out resistivity measurements by employing moderate compression between the electrodes.[9] Attempts were made to exclude air and moisture effects by passing dry hydrogen or nitrogen gas through the cell. The above referred to pressure of 80 kg/cm² was deemed sufficient to overcome intercrystalline resistance problems. One type of cell was placed in a screened glass tube and surrounded by a Dewar vessel.[10] This type of cell is reported to be suitable for the measurement of even thermally unstable organic complexes with relatively low melting points (Figure 3-3).

Another type conductivity cell[11] is shown in Figure 3-4. Here the sample is held between spring loaded copper discs, one of which can be heated. A thermocouple is soldered into each disk in order to make possible surface temperature measurements of the sample under test. Metal powder electrodes are employed for both electrical and mechanical contact. The electrodes are made by sandwich-

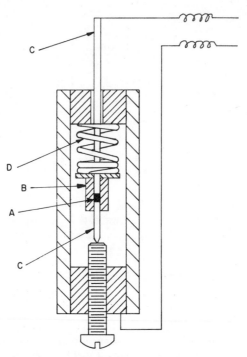

Figure 3-3. The conductivity cell for a-c and d-c measurements on molecular complexes: A. sample, B. insulating material, C. electrode, D. monic spring.

ing the powder of the material to be tested between small amounts of metal powder particles in a 1.3-cm diameter die. Thus, a one piece sandwich, about 2 mm thick, is produced in which the sample is embedded between two metal layers each of them approximately 0.05 mm thick. The entire apparatus is suitably enclosed to provide shielding against pickup rise, especially at higher temperatures.

Brown and Aftergut designed a simple conductivity cell using mercury electrodes.[12] Discs 5 to 15 mm in diameter and 1 to 3 mm thick were molded under pressure at room temperature. They were placed in a vertical position between two standard tapes socket joints which in turn were attached to L-shaped pieces of glass tubing. The glass tubes were filled with mercury which thus made contact with the disc. Only the edges of the disc were exposed

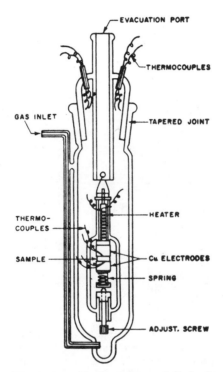

Figure 3-4. Conductivity and Seebeck coefficient measurement apparatus.

to the environment. Alternatively, gold electrodes were deposited on some specimen by vapor deposition in high vacuum.

The Film Specimen. It is well known that a great many organic compounds can be readily sublimed in vacuum at moderate temperatures without decomposition. This includes some of the polycyclic aromatic compounds which are being investigated for semiconductor properties. The evaporated films have then been employed to ascertain electronic conductivities, etc.

A typical device for the preparation of such thin films is shown in Figure 3-5.[8] A suitably purified sample of the test compound is placed into a metal gun which has been provided with a heating circuit. Evaporation is carried out under a pressure of 10^{-5} mm Hg onto a substrate, "Pyrex" glass, or quartz plate which is placed

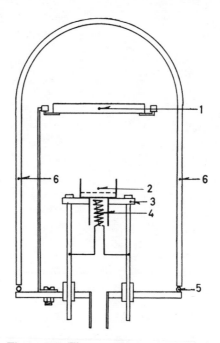

Figure 3-5. The evaporation apparatus for the aromatic hydrocarbons: 1. glass substrate, 2. nickel dish as container, 3. porcelain flat, 4. heater, 5. rubber gasket, 6. glass chamber.

opposite to the gun. The heating circuit of the gun must be carefully controlled, and the temperature difference between the gun and the substrate must be kept at a minimum. The nature of the compound to be sublimed determines the temperature necessary for evaporation in order to obtain homogeneous transparent films. For aromatic hydrocarbons the compounds with a greater number of carbon atoms require somewhat higher evaporation temperatures.[13]

Two types of electrode arrangements are generally employed to determine resistivities of thin film specimen. These are sandwich and surface-type cells. The sandwich type of conductivity cell concept is illustrated in Figure 3-6. A schematic of a surface type of conductivity cell is shown in Figure 3-7.

For sandwich-type conductivity cells a one or two micron thick film of sample specimen is deposited onto a previously metallized "Pyrex" glass plate or equivalent thereof using apparatus such as

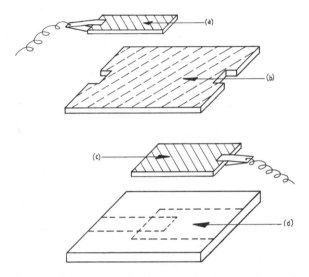

Figure 3-6. The sandwich-type conductivity cell. a and c are aluminum or lead films which serve as electrodes, b is an organic film, and d is a glass substrate.

shown in Figure 3-6. The second electrode is formed thereafter by evaporation of a metal onto the surface of the specimen film. The only conductivity path between the metal electrodes is the specimen film. Resistivity measurements with this type of cell are usually carried out in vacuo or in an inert atmosphere such as argon. Suitable electrode metals are aluminum and lead with the latter preferred by some investigators.[13]

The surface-type of conductivity cell is made by the evaporation of an organic film onto a "Pyrex" glass plate which possesses parallel electrodes that are separated by a gap of 1 to 2 mm. One quite convenient electrode material is colloidal graphite. Measurements depend markedly on the environmental atmosphere on account of the very great sensitivity of this type of conductivity cell. In particular, it has been reported that the electronic proper-

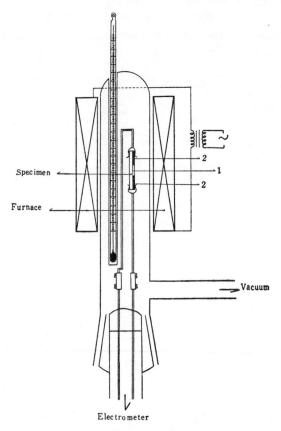

Figure 3-7. The surface-type conductivity cell placed in a glass chamber: 1. sample thin layer, 2. terminal electrode, 3. specimen, 4. furnace, 5. electrometer.

ties of anthracene are affected strikingly by a number of atmospheric gases, such as O_2, NO_2, Cl_2 etc.,[14] (see page 39 "Effect of Oxygen and other Gases"). To avoid this variable the cell is generally placed in a closed glass chamber which is evacuated to pressures lower than 10^{-5} mm Hg.

A somewhat different surface conductivity cell has been developed by Northrop and Simpson.[15] A limited amount of molten hydrocarbon is placed on a glass plate in which parallel electrodes are positioned with a narrow gap between them. The plate is at once covered by a second flat plate. The specimen is permitted to cool to below its melting point forming a thin film of hydrocarbon, from 2 to 8 microns thick. Several distinct crystalline regions make up such thin hydrocarbon films.

Some experiments have been reported by Inokuchi *et al.* on the effect of the type of resistivity measurement on the magnitude of the data obtained.[16] The results as given in Table 3-1 show fairly

Table 3-1. The Electrical Resistivity of Polycyclic Aromatics, Observed from the Various Types of Cells.

Compound	Perylene	Coronene	Violanthrene
From Bulk Specimen			
$\rho15$, ohm-cm	4×10^{18}	1.7×10^{17}	2.1×10^{14}
E, eV	1.0	0.85	0.43
From Surface Type Cell			
$\rho15$, ohm-cm	10^{13}	10^{12}–10^{13}	10^{9}
E, eV	1.1	0.85	0.45
From Sandwich Type Cell			
$\rho15$, ohm-cm	10^{18}–10^{19}	10^{17}–10^{18}	10^{14}
E, eV	1.0	0.80	0.45

good agreement in the electrical resistivity values obtained from bulk specimen and sandwich type conductivity cell measurements. There was observed, however, a rather substantial difference in the resistivity data which were obtained from surface-type and sandwich-type conductivity cells, the resistivity values from surface-type cells being much less by a factor of 10^4 to 10^5 than sandwich-type conductivity cell measurements.

It has been pointed out that in surface-type conductivity cell measurements the electrical field is applied along the surface of the specimen film. In the case of sandwich-type conductivity cells, however, the electric field is applied perpendicular to the specimen film. When a thin film is deposited from the vapor phase or from a solution, a textured structure with crystallites arranged in certain preferred orientations has been found to develop. The discrepancy in resistivity between surface-type and sandwich-type derived resistivity measurements could well be due to a significant amount of anisotropy of the resistivity of the specimen samples. More experiments are very definitely indicated to clarify this problem.

Single Crystal Specimen. A number of different experimental techniques are employed to grow single organic crystals of a size which would suffice for resistivity measurements. Growth from the vapor phase generally produces very thin flake like crystals of limited size.[17,18,19,20,21] Larger single crystals are obtained by growing from a melt[22] or from deposition from saturated solutions.[23]

Considerable work has been carried out on the growth of large single crystals of aromatic hydrocarbons. Some experiments have used a modified Bridgman type[24] of furnace consisting of two separate parts. The upper part is maintained at a temperature somewhat higher than the melting point of the material to be grown, and the lower section is kept at a lower temperature. A small quantity of a purified compound is sealed into baked glass tubing under a high vacuum or in an inert gas atmosphere. Great care is taken to avoid thermal decomposition of the compound. The container is slowly lowered through the temperature gradient set up by the heating coil in the furnace. A rate of crystal growth in the order of 1 to 2 mm/hr, has been utilized for organic crystals,[25] in contrast to 20 mm/min. for metals[26] and 1 to 4 mm/hr for ionic crystals.[27,28] The container shape also affects crystal growth.[22]

Sloan has grown ultrapure anthracene crystal from material which was purified by zone refining methods.[29] Commercially available "high purity" anthracene was zone refined with twenty-five or thirty passes after initial purification via chromatography which treatment increased the purity level by one order of magnitude from 99 to 99.9 per cent. The zone refined material had organic impurities of only one part per million. Crystal growth was accomplished in a gradient furnace. A sealed glass tube containing the anthracene was lowered at rates of as high as 2 to 3 cm/day into the colder region of the furnace. A single crystal of a size suitable for resistivity measurements was grown in 8 to 10 days.

Alternatively, large single crystals of organic compounds can be grown from their solutions by the slow evaporation of solvent over a long period. One of the more important problems is to select a suitable solvent. The essential feature of the selection is to create a density and temperature gradient within the solution so that the crystal will grow slowly and will remain suspended during its growth. Anthracene single crystals ranging in thickness from 4 to 80 μ and from 0.5 to 2 cm^2 in area have been prepared by the above method from ethylene dichloride or xylene solutions.[23]

The electrical contact between a single crystal and the electrodes is very important. Different contact methods have been considered to obtain such contacts. Aquadag and silver paint have been frequently used.

Other Electronic Properties Measurements

Only a limited amount of work has been carried out on the determination of other important electronic properties including the Hall effect, Seebeck effect, mobility, and so on. This is one area of study in the organic semiconductor field which very definitely requires much more attention than has thus far been given to it. Such measurements promise to be particularly important with the newer organic semiconductor compounds which in many cases possess a remarkable combination of properties well worthy of such investigations.

One of the most valuable tools for the characterization of semiconducting material is Hall effect measurements. It has been repeatedly stated that the Hall effect is very difficult to observe in organic materials, primarily because of the very low mobilities. One of the few published investigations in which such measurements have been reported is the work of Epstein and Wildi on poly-phthalocyanines.[30] Samples for Hall effect and resistivity measurements were made by compacting the test material under pressures of more than 20,000 psi into rectangular parallelopipeds 0.9 × 0.3 × 0.8 cm in dimension. The necessary electrical contacts were obtained by silver paints or evaporated silver films. The sample was placed on a lavite sample holder with electrical connections to external circuits arranged through glass-metal seals. The sample holder was placed in a Vycor tube so arranged as to permit measurements in different atmospheres. A schematic of the experimental set up is shown in Figure 3-8.

A Leeds and Northrup type K3 potentiometer and a Kintel electronic galvanometer were used to obtain d-c measurements. A Varian 10-cm magnet with regulated supply was used to obtain the d-c magnetic field. Measurements were made as a function of temperature in the range from 25° to above 250°C.

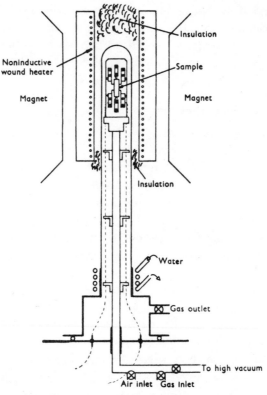

Figure 3-8. Experimental arrangement for measurement of electrical resistivity and Hall effect.

Brennan and his co-workers also measured Hall effect on pyrolyzed polyacrylonite (see page 133). A considerable number of works on Hall effect measurements have been published on various carbon samples (see Chapter 6, Electronic Carbons).

There are few references in the literature to a determination of the Seebeck coefficient.[31,32,33,34]

One type of apparatus for measuring the Seebeck coefficients is shown in Figure 3-9. A layer of the powdered polymer was placed between two platinum foils, which were insulated electrically by means of mica sheets from aluminum blocks. The powder was compacted by compressing the whole assembly. One of the blocks was heated by inserting a pencil type soldering iron to establish a suitable thermal gradient. The temperatures were determined by platinum-platinum/10 per cent rhodium thermocouples attached

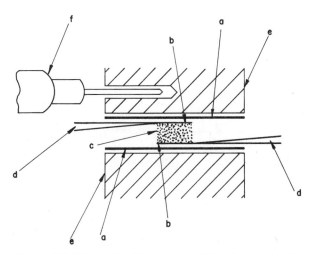

Figure 3-9. Schematic diagram of cell for thermoelectric power determinations. A. mica insulator layers, B. Pt foil electrodes, C. compressed powder sample, D. Pt-Pt: 10 per cent Rh thermocouples, E. heater blocks, F. heater. (From Reference 34)

to the foils. The Seebeck voltages were measured by means of the platinum leads of the thermocouples. Voltages were measured with a Leeds and Northrup K-3 potentiometer. Absolute Seebeck coefficients of the polymers were obtained by correcting for the Seebeck coefficients of the platinum.

The direct measurement of carrier mobilities is considered important for elucidating the mechanism of charge transfer in organic solids. Kepler[35] and LeBlanc[36] succeeded independently in the determination of the mobility of highly purified anthracene. The basic experimental arrangements have been described and are shown in Figure 3-10. They consists essentially of an anthracene crystal which is placed between two electrodes, one of which is connected to a voltage supply and the other to a resistor. The voltage across the resistor is measured as a function of time by means of an amplifier-oscilloscope. This arrangement causes the electrodes to act like the plates of a parallel plate capacitor making physical contact to the crystal unnecessary. Therefore, when ¼-mil Mylar film was placed between the crystal and the electrodes, no changes in experimental results were obtained.

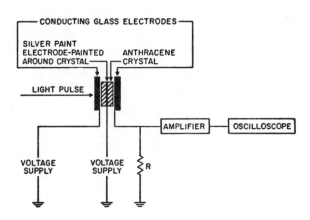

Figure 3-10. Block diagram of the experimental arrangement.

Light pulses of very short duration (1 to 2 μsec) applied to the crystal through one of the electrodes are very strongly absorbed and create carriers near the illuminated surface. The motion of the carriers in the crystals is similar to a polarization of a dielectric in a capacitor. The current in the external circuit is proportional to the number of charge carriers moving times their average velocity.

Effect of Impurities

Considering the very great body of work which has been devoted to the study of the effects of impurities on the electronic properties of inorganic semiconductors, investigations on the role of impurities in organic semiconductors have been quite limited. There is at this time no agreement on the answer to such fundamental questions as to how pure an organic semiconductor must be before conductivity measurements should be attempted and/or which impurities are electronically active. It must also be pointed out that there are significant differences in the measured conductivity values obtained by different investigators who were using similar measuring techniques on the same compound.

The problem of ascertaining the effects of impurities on organic semiconductors is complicated because both inorganic and organic impurities must be considered. The determination of inorganic impurities can be carried out using essentially the same methods which have been so successful with inorganic semiconductors. Emission spectroscopy has been shown to have considerable merit for metallic elements in small quantities. Determination of organic impurities and their elimination—if so desired—presents a new and difficult problem.

The usual methods of purifying organic compounds include the well known techniques of recrystallization, solvent extraction, distillation, sublimation, chromatography, etc. In addition zone refining methods have been considered and used on a limited scale. In general it has not been shown that any single method possesses significant advantages over others. Suitability of a purification method is frequently dependent on the chemical and physical properties of the compound under study. Frequently more than one purification method is required to obtain adequate purification.[37] It must however be emphasized that the term "purity" means different things to the organic chemist than to the researcher engaged in studies of inorganic semiconductors. There are really no known effective methods for separating trace organic impurities from organic compounds. The development of such methods is a task well worthy of the attention of the analytical chemist. Pending development of such analytical skills determinations of organic impurities, particularly in trace quantities, will at best be precarious. Radioactive tracers are one possibility, as is neutron activation for certain elements.

Probably one of the earliest studies relating to impurity effects on organic semiconductor electronic properties is the work of Northrop and Simpson on the effect of impurities on the dark conductivity of anthracene evaporated films.[13] These investigators prepared solid solutions of tetracene, pentacene, perylene, and anthracene in chrysene, pyrene, and anthracene. Conductivities were then measured as a function of temperature using various concentrations in the region of 0.1 mole per cent. At high temperatures the conductivity was found to vary with the activation energy pertaining to the solvent but at lower temperatures the slope of the $\left(\log \sigma, \dfrac{1}{T}\right)$ curve went over to another, smaller activation energy characteristic of the solute. Table 3-2 shows the results obtained for the pure polyacenes, and, for those used as solutes, the mean value of the impurity E in the three solvents.

Table 3-2. Effect of Impurities on Activation Energy of Polyecenes.

Compound	E, eV, Pure Polyacene	E, eV, as Impurity
Anthracene	0.97	
Pyrene	1.01	
Chrysene	1.10	
Tetracene	0.85	0.63
Pentacene	0.75	0.50
Perylene	0.98	0.80
Anthanthrene	0.80	0.58

Parkyns and Ubbelohde have measured the electronic properties of isoviolanthrene and isoviolanthrone of varying degrees of chemical purity. They found significant differences in electronic properties as a function of the purification process used.[37a]

Previous mention has been made of the fact that various investigators working with the same chemical compound have obtained different quantitative results of the electronic properties. Table 3-3 illustrates this for naphthalene and anthracene.[39] Little useful information is available on the purity of the compounds which were measured.

Okamoto and co-workers have measured the electrical resistivities of naphthalene and anthracene which had been previously purified by various methods.[39] The metallic impurity concentrations of the variously purified polyacenes were known via emission spectrographic analyses. Typical data are shown in Tables 3-4 and 3-5. It is to be noted that the measurements showed significant differences in both the ρ and E values at different metallic impurity concentrations. However, it was not determined whether the metallic impurities were present as the free metal, an inorganic

Table 3-3. Conduction Energy Gap (E) of Naphthalene and Anthracene.

Author	Temperature Range, °C	E, eV	Comments
Naphthalene			
Pick and Wissman[a]	60–75	1.85	Single crystals (in vacuo)
Riehl[b]	20–75	0.70	Single crystals (in dry air)
Brown and Aftergut[c]	46–63	1.35	Disc (in N_2 atmosphere)
	36–63	1.40	Disc (in air)
Anthracene			
Mette and Pick[d]	80–200	0.83	Single crystal
Inokuchi[e]	50–150	1.35	Single crystal
Riehl[b]	20–60	0.75	Single crystal
Northrop and Simpson	25–80	0.97	Films
Eley, Parfitt, Perry and Taysum[g]	70–204	0.83	Polycrystalline

[a] Pick, H., and Wissman, W., Z. Physik, **138**, 436 (1954).
[b] Riehl, N., Ann. Physik, **20**, 93 (1957).
[c] Brown, G. P., and Aftergut, S., Proc. of the Princeton University Conference on Semiconduction in Molecular Solids, 1960.
[d] Mette, H., and Pick, H., Z. Physik, **134**, 566 (1953).
[e] Inokuchi, H., Bull. Chem. Soc. Japan, **29**, 131 (1956).
[f] Northrop, D. C., and Simpson, O., Proc. Roy. Soc., **A234**, 124 (1956).
[g] Eley, D. D., Parfitt, G. D., Perry, M. J., and Taysum, D. H., Trans. Faraday Soc., **49**, 79 (1953).

Table 3-4. Effect of Metallic Impurities on the Resistivity of Naphthalene.

Sample Number and Purification Method	NA 2 As Obtained	NA 5 2 Vacuum Sublimations	NA 6 4 Vacuum Sublimations	NA 4 Sulfuric Acid Treatment and 2 Vacuum Sublimations
Spectrographic Analysis				
Si	0.00X	0.000X[a]	0.0000X	NF
Mg	0.00X	0.000X	0.0000X	0.000X
Ag	0.00X	NF[b]	NF	NF
Fe	0.00X	0.0000X	NF	NF
Ca	0.000X	0.000X	NF	NF
Cu	0.0000X	0.0000X	NF	NF
Al	0.000X	0.000X	NF	NF
Calculated ρ_0, ohm-cm	1.0×10^{-33}	1.40×10^{-15}	1.50×10^{-9}	3.66×10^{-16}
Calculated E, eV	3.00	1.84	1.49	2.33
Temperature range, °C	40–70°	40–70°	40–70°	40–70°

[a] Estimated value: 0.00X = 0.001–0.009 %.
[b] Elements are checked but not found.

Table 3-5. Effect of Metallic Impurities on the Resistivity of Anthracene.

Sample Number and Purification Method	A-1 As Obtained	A-2 2 Vacuum Sublimations	A-3 4 Vacuum Sublimations	A-4[a] Hydrochloric Acid Treatment and 2 Vacuum Sublimations	A-5 Hydrochloric Acid Treatment and 2 Vacuum Sublimations
		Spectrographic Analysis			
Mg	0.00X	0.00X (low)	0.000X	0.000X	0.000X
Si	0.00X	0.00X (low)	0.000X	0.000X	0.000X
Al	0.00X	0.00X (low)	NF	0.000X	NF
Ni	0.00X	0.000X	NF	NF	NF
Ca	0.00X	0.00X	0.000X	0.00X (low)	0.000X
Fe	0.00X (low[b])	0.000X	0.000X	0.000X	0.000X
Cu	0.000X	0.000X (low)	NF	0.000X	NF
Cr	0.000X	NF	NF	NF	NF
Pb	0.000X	0.0000X	NF	NF	NF
Na	0.000X	0.000X	0.000X (low)	0.0X	NF
K	0.000X	0.000X	NF	0.00X	NF
Ag	0.0000X	0.0000X	NF	NF	NF
Sn	0.0000X	NF	NF	NF	NF
Mn	0.0000X	NF	NF	NF	NF
Calculated ρ_0, ohm-cm	4.58×10^{-3}	1.70×10^2	5.62×10^2	9.48×10[c] 1.06×10^2[d] 1.85×10^2[e] 9.66×10[f]	5.34
Calculated, E, eV	1.13	0.832	0.812	0.860[c] 0.846[d] 0.859[e] 0.866[f]	0.946
Temperature range, °C	45–160°	45–160°	45–160°	45–160°	45–160°

[a] The surprisingly high contents of sodium and potassium may have been introduced inadvertently during the washing process by water.
[b] Estimated value: 0.00X (low) = 0.001–0.005%.
[c] Normal.
[d] Same material (A-4) different pellet.
[e] Repeat run on same pellet as (c).
[f] Same material, different pellet measured under oxygen and moisture free nitrogen atmosphere.

salt, or somehow chemically combined with the polyacene, etc. Furthermore, it was not determined what the effects of specific metal impurities on electronic properties are.

Additional investigations along similar lines are suggested to broaden our understanding of the effects of impurities on the electronic properties of organic semiconductors. It is realized that such measurements present many difficult problems, especially when organic impurities are to be studied.

Eley and Parfitt have carried out spectrographic analyses of metallic impurities in phthalocyanine samples.[4] Typical analyses are shown in Table 3-6. Three samples were examined with total

Table 3-6. Spectrographic Analysis of Phthalocyanine Samples (%).

	(1)	(ii)	(ii) RS	(iii) RS	(iii) Res
Fe	0.1	0.01	—	—	0.1
Si	—	0.1–1.0	0.1–1.0	0.1	0.1–1.0
Mn	0.1	0.1–1.0	0.1	0.1–1.0	0.1
Mg	—	0.1–1.0	0.1–1.0	—	0.1
Al	—	—	—	—	—
Cu	—	0.01	0.01–0.1	—	0.01–1.0
Pb	0.001	0.001–0.01	0.001–0.01	0.001	0.001
Bi	—	—	0.01–0.1	—	0.1
Ca	—	—	—	—	—
Sn	0.001	—	0.01–0.1	0.001	—
Sb	—	—	—	0.1	1.0
Ag	0.001	—	—	—	—
Ni	—	—	—	—	0.1

RS: Sample after recrystallization from quinoline and sublimation.
Res: Residue left from previous sublimation of sample.

impurity contents in the order (i) 0.2 per cent (ii) RS, 0.2 to 1.3 per cent (iii) RS, 0.3 to 1.0 per cent. The data obtained, which are shown in Table 3-7, do not, however, indicate substantial differences in their electronic properties.

Table 3-7. Effect of Impurities on the Electronic Properties of Phthalocyanines.

Sample	$\log \rho_0$	E, eV
(i)	-1.37 ± 0.06	0.73
(ii) RS	-2.06 ± 0.12	0.76
(iii) RS	-2.45 ± 0.07	0.74

Brown and Aftergut have also been interested in the effects of impurities on organic semiconductors.[39] Figure 3-11 shows the specific resistivities of two different solutions of phenazine in naphthalene as a function of temperatures. The differences are significant but not major. Some theoretical considerations have also been described.

The effects of impurities and radiation damage on the electrical properties of carbons will also be considered in Chapter 7. As has

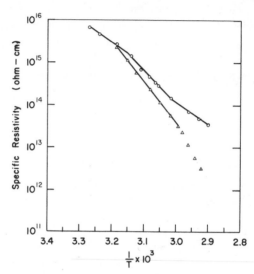

Figure 3-11. Specific resistivities of solution of phenazine in naphthalene
$\bigcirc$ = 0.1% phenazine in naphthalene, cooling curve
$\triangle$ = 10% phenazine in naphthalene, cooling curve

been indicated above, the subject has hardly been approached and is well worth further study and investigation. It can be anticipated that a better understanding of the effects of impurities may also help increase our knowledge of the basic mechanisms of electron transport in organic solids.

Effect of Pressure

The application of ultra high pressures to any material will cause increases in the kinetic energy of its electrons. The quantum theory

suggests that when the kinetic energy of the electrons is increased
to the energy level which will permit them to free themselves from
the electric fields of their nuclei, any material will become metallic.
It has been calculated by Chandrasekhar (1951) that the pressures
needed to cause the complete breakdown of matter into a homogeneous mass of free electrons and nuclei are in the order of 10^{10}
atmospheres.[40] Such high pressures are not experimentally attain-
able at this time. However, recent experiments which have been
carried out at significantly lower though conventionally considered
extremely high pressures, 10^4 to 10^5 atmospheres, have shown substantial decreases in the electrical resistivity with increasing pressure. The effects of high pressure on the electrical resistivity of
semiconductor materials are now being variously investigated for a
better understanding of electronic conduction mechanism as well as
for the discovery of novel phases with, it is hoped, unique and valuable properties.

Most of the experiments relating to the effects of high pressure
applications on materials have been carried out on metals. The
many investigations of Bridgman are particularly noteworthy.[41]
Changes in conductivity amounting to about two-fold were re-
portedly obtained with external pressures in the order of 10^5 atmospheres. More recently the preparation of diamond from graphite
and the discovery of a cubic form of boronnitride have been accomplished by high pressure methods.[42] Also the effects of high pressures on inorganic semiconductor materials have been investigated.
The conductivity of silicon increased for pressures up to 30,000
atmospheres.[43] Similar results were obtained for germanium.[44]
Various other elements such as boron, phosphorus, sulfur, and
iodine and also intermetallic compounds have been investigated
with about the same general effect of pressure on conductivity
observed.[45]

Organic solids are quite compressible considering the relative
weakness of their intermolecular forces. The application of even
moderate pressures can bring about large orbital overlaps between
adjacent molecules during compression. This can be expected to be
reflected in a significant increase of their electrical conductivity.
However early studies on the conductivity of organic materials indicated that pressure has little effect. Thus Eley, et al., [4,9] Akamatu

and Inokuchi,[48] and other workers implied the existence of a limiting pressure above which the electrical conductivity of organic materials does not change. This limiting pressure was defined by Akamatu and Inokuchi as around 80 kg/cm². Eley, *et al.* have attributed moderate changes in conductivity and the activation energy to packing effects upon powders. Brown and Aftergut have stated that pressurization serves only to remove macroscopic voids in the samples under investigation.[12] The results of Inokuchi on isoviolanthrone shown in Table 3-8 below are typical of such experiments.[7]

Table 3-8. Pressure Dependence of Resistivity of Isoviolanthrone.

Pressure, kg/cm²	ρ_{15}, ohm-cm	ρ_0, ohm-cm	ϵ (2kT)
3×10^2	5×10^9	1.3×10^3	0.75
4.2×10^3	8.4×10^7	3.0×10	0.74
6.3×10^3	2.6×10^7	2.2×10	0.69
8.4×10^3	1.2×10^7	1.0×10	0.68

A more recent study of the effects of pressure on the electrical conductivity of metal free and copper phthalocyamines has given significantly different results.[46] The experiments were carried out at temperatures between 25 and 200°C in the pressure range of 1,000 to 50,000 atmospheres. At constant temperatures the conductivities were found to increase markedly with greater pressures. Also the conductivities increased with increasing temperatures at constant pressure. The data of Figure 3-12 and Figure 3-13 illustrate these results.

The effect of pressures up to several hundred kilobars on the electrical conductivity of seven fused ring aromatic compounds comprising two polyacenes and five quinones has been determined by Samara and Drickamer.[47] A rather rapid increase of conductivity was obtained at lower pressure followed by a marked leveling off at above 200 to 250 kilobars. This leveling off has been associated with the rapid decrease in compressibility at high pressures as observed by Bridgman. The resistance at high pressures of different compounds varied by several orders of magnitude and were con-

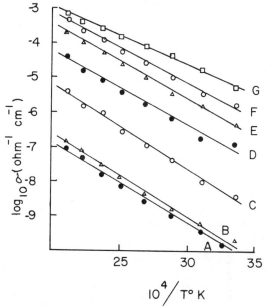

Figure 3-12. Phthalocyanine, $\log_{10} \sigma$ against $10^4/T$ at 25-200°C at various pressures; A 1.25, B 2.5, C 6.25, D 12.5, E 25, F 37.5, and G 50 kbars.

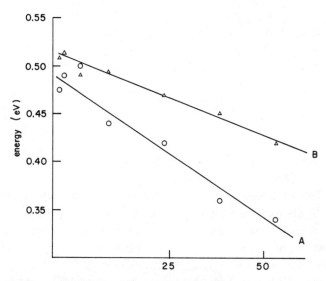

Figure 3-13. Variation of E with pressure for (A) β phthalocyanine and (B) copper phthalocyanine.

sidered related to the amount of overlap between adjacent molecules in the unit cell. Activation energies at the highest pressures studied were about one sixth of the atmospheric pressure values.

The compounds studied were the following: isoviolanthrone, violanthrone, pyranthrone, dibenzo (α,h)pyrene-7,14-dione, dibenzo (c,d,j,k) pyrene-6,12-dione, pentacene, tetracene, and anthracene.

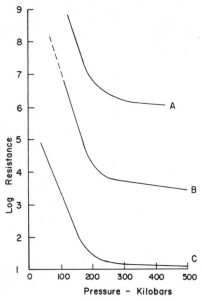

Figure 3-14. Resistance *vs* pressure
for polyacenes and quinones.
A = Tetracene
B = Pyranthrone
C = Violanthrone

The results are summarized in Figure 3-14. Relative compressibilities are shown in Figure 3-15.

The effect of pressure on the electrical conductivity of polymeric organics is also under study. Pohl and Opp investigated the effect of pressure on organic semiconducting polymers prepared by the condensation of 1-hydroxyanthraquinone and 1,8-naphthalic anhydride in the presence of zinc chloride at 360°C.[48] The conductivity increased reversibly up to pressures of 60,000 atmospheres—the highest measured in this study.

Similar studies by Pohl and Engelhardt showed a smooth change of conductivity with pressure for other polymers as well.[49] The activation energies decreased with increasing pressure. Pohl, Rembaum and Henry, found that certain organic polymers of the poly-

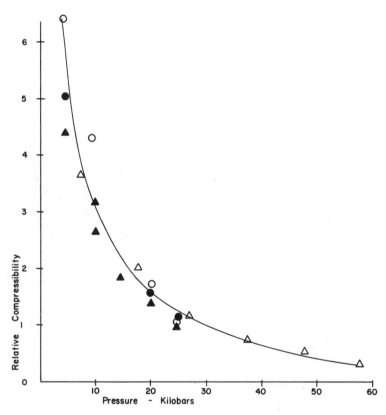

Figure 3-15. Relative compressibility *vs* pressure—molecular crystals.

● = Anthracene
○ = Naphthalene
▲ = Anthroquinone
△ = Sulfur

acenequinone type possess a very high piezo-resistive coefficient.[50] "Compared to metals which change up to twofold in a given pressure ranges these materials change by a factor of 100-fold or more"[50] presumably on account of the easily compressible intermolecular distances and energy barriers for electron transfer. The conductivity also increased at higher temperatures. Results for a typical polymer system are shown in Figure 3-16.

Hatano has also carried out studies on this problem.[51] Polyacetylenes prepared by Ziegler-type catalysts were investigated. The application of only moderate pressures was found to result in some increase of the conductivity.

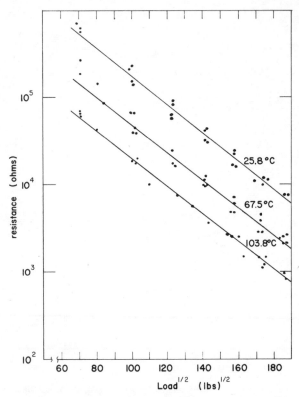

Figure 3-16. Observed resistance *vs* load for the PAQR polymer obtained from condensing terphenyl with pyromellitic dianhydride.

A review of the work reported to date shows that no novel phases, etc., have been uncovered thus far. The phenomena measured were all reversible, i.e., the resistivities increased again upon relaxation of the applied pressure. Also, substantial pressure applications in terms of thousands of atmospheres are apparently required to obtain large conductivity gains.

Effect of Oxygen and Other Gases

The effects of various gases on the electronic properties of organic semiconductive materials has not yet been fully investigated. A review of pertinent literature references shows that the role of oxygen in photo and dark conductivity of selected organic solids has been experimentally studied. Little attention has thus far been given to the effects of other gases. As for oxygen, it is recognized that it can affect organic materials in different ways such as absorption, adsorption, oxidation, and initiation of reactions. The differentiation of such effects is often difficult but may be important for an adequate understanding of the role of this gas.

Riehl has reported the total amount of oxygen absorbed by naphthalene crystals in the order of 10^{-7} grams of oxygen per gram of naphthalene at an oxygen pressure of 1 atmosphere and at ambient temperatures.[52] This value was obtained by radioactivation methods. The effect on electrical conductivity was not studied, however.

In an earlier investigation by Pick and Weissman, the electrical properties of single crystals of naphthalene were measured as a function of the oxygen pressure.[53] It was found that in an atmosphere of oxygen the activation energy decreased as the oxygen pressure was raised. Thus, the activation energy dropped from 1.85 to 0.75 eV as the oxygen pressure was increased from 0.1 to 2.0 atmospheres. Oxygen pressure increases from 2.0 to 5.0 atmospheres did not result in further changes of the activation energy. The observed activation energy changes were reversible.

Vartanyan had found that the photoconductivity of a thin anthracene film deposit increased when oxygen was admitted to the surrounding.[54] Chynoweth reported rather similar observations on crystalline anthracene deposits.[55] If the oxygen was replaced by another gas such as nitrogen or argon, there was no increase of photoconductivity. The increase in photoconductivity with oxygen was attributed to the photooxidation of the surface. It has also been reported that the electronic properties of anthracene are somewhat affected by a number of atmospheric gases such as oxygen, nitrogen, and sulfur dioxides, etc.[56]

It might also be noted the specific conductance of benzene solutions saturated with dry air has been found to be increased by a factor of 10 from 0.1×10^{-16} ohm^{-1} cm^{-1} to 6.9×10^{-15} ohm^{-1} cm^{-1}. This has been related to the effect of oxygen on the conductance of benzene.[57]

Additional investigations are indicated to better ascertain the effects of various gases on the electrical properties of organic semiconductive materials. As indicated above the exact mode of interaction of the gas with the organic material should be of particular interest.

References

1. Huggins, C. M., "Organic Crystal Symposium", Ottawa, Canada, Oct. 1962.
2. Dunlap, W. Crawford, Jr., "Methods of Experimental Physics" in "Conductivity Measurements on Solids," New York, Academic Press, Inc., 1959.
3. Hund, A., "High Frequency Measurements," New York, McGraw Hill Book Co., Inc., 1951.
4. Eley, D. D., and Parfitt, J. D., *Trans. Faraday Soc.*, **51**, 1529 (1955).
5. Blanck, A. R., "Ultra High Resistance Measurements of Plastics," Report PB 161784, Picatinny Arsenal, Dover, N.J.
6. Kennedy, J. K., *Rev. Sci. Inst.*, **33**, 773 (1962).
7. Inokuchi, H., *Bull. Chem. Soc. Japan*, **28**, 570 (1955).
8. Akamatu, H., and Inokuchi, H., "Solid State Physics," Vol. 2, Ed. by F. Seitz and D. Turnbull, New York, Academic Press, 1961.
9. Eley, D. D., Parfill, G. D., Perry, M. J., and Tsysum, D. H., *Trans. Faraday Soc.*, **49**, 79 (1953).
10. Eley, D. D., Inokuchi, H., and Willis, M. R., *Discussions Faraday Soc.*, **29**, 54 (1959).
11. Labes, M. M., Seho, R., and Bose, M., *J. Chem. Phys.*, **33**, 868 (1960).
12. Brown, G. P., and Aftergut, S., Proc. of Princeton University Conference in Semiconduction Molecular Solids, Princeton, N.J., 1960.
13. Northrop, D. C., and Simpson, D., *Proc. Roy. Soc.*, **A234**, 124 (1956).
14. Compton, D. M. J., and Eaddington, T. C., *J. Chem. Phys.*, **25**, 1075 (1956).
15. Northrop, D. C., and Simpson, D., *Proc. Roy. Soc.*, **A244**, 377 (1958).
16. Inokuchi, H., Kuroda, H., and Akamatu, H. *Bull. Chem. Soc. Japan*, **34**, 749 (1961).
17. Buckley, H. E., "Crystal Growth," New York, John Wiley & Sons, Inc., 1951.
18. Dawson, I. M., and Vand, V., *Proc. Roy. Soc.*, **A206**, 555 (1951).
19. Brandstatter, M., *Z. Elektrochem*, **56**, 968 (1952).
20. Craig, D. P., and Hobbins, P. C., *J. Chem. Soc.*, 2309 (1955).
21. Lawson, W. D., and Neilsen, S., "Preparation of Single Crystals." London, Butterworths, 1958.
22. Sherwood, J. N., and Thomson, S. J., *J. Sci. Inst.*, **37**, 242 (1960).
23. Kallmann, H., and Pope, M., *Rev. Sci. Inst.*, **29**, 993 (1958).
24. Bridgman, P. W., *Proc. Amer. Acad. Arts Sci.*, **60**, 305 (1925).
25. Scott, K. T. B., Hutchinson, S. K., and Lapage, R., A.W.R.E. Report No. 0-4/53 (1953).
26. Goss, A. J., and Weintroub, S., *Nature, London*, **167**, 349 (1951).

27. Menzies, A. C., and Skinner, J., *Discuss. Faraday Soc.* **5**, 306 (1949).
28. Stockbarger, D. C., *Discuss. Faraday Soc.*, **5**, 294 (1949).
29. Hein, E., "Why They Study Strange Organic Solids," *DuPont Magazine*, May–June 1961.
30. Epstein, A., and Wildi, B. S., *J. Chem. Phys.*, **32**, 324 (1960).
31. Labes, M. M., Sehr, R. A., and Bose, M., Proc. of the Princeton University Conference on "Semiconduction in Molecular Solids," Princeton, N.J., 1960.
32. Fielding, P. E., and Gutman, F. J., *J. Chem. Phys.*, **26**, 411 (1957).
33. Winslow, F. H., Baker, W. O., and Yager, W. A., *J. Am. Chem. Soc.*, **77**, 4751 (1955).
34. Pohl, H. A., Bornmann, J. A., and Itoh, W., "Organic Semiconductors," Ed. by J. J. Brophy and J. W. Buttrey, New York, The MacMillan Co., 1962.
35. Kepler, R. G., *Phys. Rev.*, **119**, 1226 (1960).
36. LeBlanc, O. H., Jr., *J. Chem. Phys.*, **33**, 626 (1960).
37. Armington, A. F., Kennedy, J. K., Silcox, N. W., and Nussbaum, S., "Classical Purification Techniques," Electronics Research Directorate, Air Force Cambridge Research Laboratories, Bedford, Mass. (1961).
37a. Parkyns, N., and Ubbelohde, A. R., *J. Chem. Soc.*, 4188 (1960).
38. Okamoto, Y., Huang, F. T., Gordon, A., Brenner, W., and Rubin, B., "Organic Semiconductors," Ed. by J. J. Brophy and J. W. Buttrey, New York, The Macmillan Co., 1962.
39. Brown, G. P., and Aftergut, S., "Organic Semiconductors," Ed.: J. J. Brophy and J. J. Buttrey, New York, The Macmillan Co., 1962.
40. Chandrasekhar, S., "Astrophysics," Ed. by J. A. Hynek, New York, McGraw-Hill Book Co., 1951.
41. Bridgman, P. W., *Proc. Am. Acad. Arts & Sci.*, **81**, 165 (1952).
42. Wentorf, R. H., *Chem. Eng.* (Oct. 16, 1961),
43. Paul, W., and Pearson, G. L., *Phys. Rev.*, **98**, 1755 (1955).
44. Paul, W., and Brooks, H., *ibid.*, **94**, 1128 (1954).
45. Hamann, S. D., *Aust. J. Chem.* **11**, 391 (1958).
46. Bradley, R. S., Grace, J. D., and Munro, D. C., *Trans. Faraday Soc.*, **46**, 777 (1962).
47. Samara, G. A., and Drickamer, H. G., *J. Chem. Phys.*, **37**, 474 (1962).
48. Pohl, H. A., and Opp, D. A., Abst. of papers at Chicago, Ill., Div. Phys. Chem., ACS Meeting, Sept. 1961.
49. Pohl, H. A., and Engelhardt, E. H., *ibid.*, Div. Polymer Chem.
50. Pohl, H. A., Rembaum, A., and Henry, A., *J. Am. Chem. Soc.*, **84**, 2699 (1962).
51. Hatano, M., Kogyo, Kogaku, *Zasshi.*, **65**, 723 (1962).
52. Riehl, N., in "Symposium on Electrical Conductivity in Organic Solids," Ed. by H. Kallman and M. Silver, New York, Interscience Publishers, 1962.
53. Pick, H., and Weissman, W., *Z. Physik*, **138**, 436 (1954).
54. Vartanyan, A. T., *Doklady Akad. Nauk-USSR*, **71**, 641 (1950).
55. Chynoweth, A. G., *J. Chem. Phys.*, **22**, 1029 (1954).
56. Schneider, W. G., and Waddington, T. C., *J. Chem. Phys.*, **25**, 358 (1956).
57. Foster, E. O., *J. Chem. Phys.*, **37**, 1021, (1962).

4

Monomeric Organic Compounds

The current revival of interest in the electronic characteristics of organic solids is reflected by a considerable increase in
the number of investigations dealing with the measurement of
electrical conductivities and related properties as well as attempts
at finding a firmer theoretical explanation of the nature of the
conduction mechanisms involved. A considerable body of data has
thus been assembled on organic conductivities. Significant discrep-
ancies in the observed values may be related to different methods
of measurement and frequently unspecified or questionable purities
of the test specimens. Measurements on single crystals are still
quite limited, however, although they are preferable as they permit
correlation of crystal structure with pertinent electronic properties.
The majority of the available data has been obtained with compressed powder and film specimen. Interfacial effects, possible surface conduction, and anisotropy considerations make the usefulness
of such polycrystalline measurements of restricted value. Also,
available data on the electronic properties are largely limited to
conductivity measurements and determinations of the energy gap.
This chapter summaries the experimental data for monomeric
organic compounds developed to date.

One of the most interesting aspects of the studies of the electronic characteristics of organic solids is the relationship to their
chemical structure. Much work remains yet to be done to establish

a correlation between electronic properties and chemical structure. One early investigation was carried out on a series of polycyclic aromatics differing in the number of condensed rings. It was found that the electrical resistivity and energy gap decrease with a larger number of condensed aromatic rings.[1] The correlation between the energy gap with the number of π electrons for linear polyacenes and condensed naphthalenes are attempted.[14] While in both cases the energy gap decreases with a greater number of π electrons, the

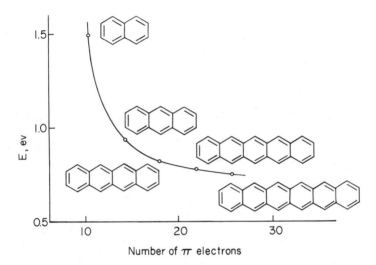

Figure 4-1. Correlation of energy gap with number of π electrons of linear polyacenes. (Data from Refs. 8 and 14)

relationships representing this change are expressed by different curves for the polyacene and the naphthalene series as shown in Figures 4-1 and 4-2.

Experiments were carried also out on the conductivity characteristics of different biphenyl compounds.[15] The energy gap and the conductivities decreased up to quaterphenyl but remained constant from there on even for poly p-phenyl (Figure 4-3). For the high molecular weight p-phenyls the relative constancy of resistivity and energy gap as a function of the number of π electrons may be due to an unfavorable structure with respect to intermolecular overlapping, i.e., the phenyl groups may be twisted in

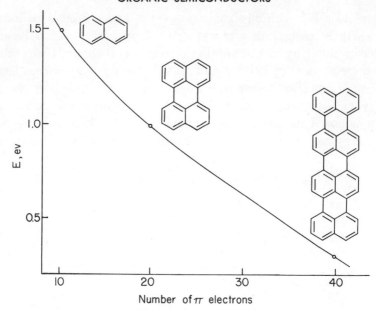

Figure 4-2. Correlation of energy gap with number of π electrons of condensed naphthalene. (Data from Refs 19 and 23)

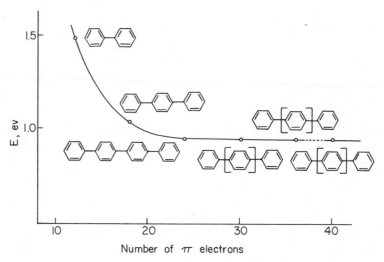

Figure 4-3. Correlation of energy gap with number of π electrons of biphenyl system. (Data from Ref 15)

order to minimize steric hindrance of the ortho hydrogens. The preparation of large conjugated compounds with a coplanar structure may exhibit significantly higher conductivities and correspondingly lower energy gaps. Such compounds still remain to be synthesized.

A comparison was made of the electrical conductivity of selected compounds with quinoid structures and the corresponding hydrocarbons. Compounds having quinoid structures are apparently more conductive. Thus, the conductivity of isoviolanthrone, 10^{-9} ohm^{-1}-cm^{-1} is four orders of magnitude higher than that of the analogous hydrocarbon isoviolanthrene.

Efforts have been made to relate the electronic properties of phthalocyanine compounds to their chemical structure. The presence of the metal atom or its identity in the porphyrin ring has relatively little effect on conductivity and energy gap.[28] A more comprehensive study of these interesting compounds which will take into account such factors as purity, polymorphism, and experimental conditions, may help to further elucidate this effect.

Crystal structure is another important consideration. The previously mentioned phthalocyanines exhibit three polymorphic forms called α, β and γ. The α form is reported to possess a lower resistivity than the β form.[11] In hexamethyl benzene a phase transition occurs from the triclinic to the orthorhombic form above 110°C. However, no change of the energy gap was observed.[2] Further studies along these lines may contribute significantly to a better understanding of the conduction process involved.

The electronic properties of isomeric compounds present an interesting problem. Consideration shall be given to cis-trans and d-l optical isomers. Other as yet unexplored problems concern inter and intramolecular hydrogen bonds, tautomerism, etc.

There is increasing interest in a correlation of electronic properties such as energy gap with various physical characteristics including optical absorption spectra, resonance energies, etc. It has been reported that the value of the spectral threshold of photoconduction is in good agreement with thermally obtained energy gap measurements for certain polyaromatics.[3]

The available experimental data of many organic solids are shown in the following Table 4-1.

Table 4-1. The Electrical Resistivity and Energy Gaps of Monomeric Organic Compounds.

Substance and Structure	E, eV	ρ ohm-cm	ρ_0 ohm-cm	Comments	Ref.
1. Hydrocarbons					
benzene	0.41		2×10^8	liquid form	4
o-xylene	0.45		3×10^9	liquid form	4
m-xylene	0.41		1×10^8	liquid form	4
p-xylene	0.41		1×10^8	liquid form	4
mesitylene	0.19		2×10^{14}	liquid form	4
naphthalene	1.8	10^{19} (15°)	1×10^{-13}	single crystal	5
	0.7		10^5	single crystal	6
	1.40		10^{-7}	powder in air atmosphere	7
	1.35		2.0×10^{-6}	powder in nitrogen atmosphere	7
	1.15	2.8×10^{14} (50°)	1.5×10^{-9}		

MONOMERIC ORGANIC COMPOUNDS 47

compound					
anthracene 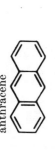	0.83	1.3×10^{14} (15°)	0.5	single crystal in a-b plane	9
	1.35	10^{22} (15°)	10^{-2}	single crystal perpendicular to a-b plane	10
	0.75	—	—	same as above	6
tetracene	0.83	7×10^{15} (15°)	3×10^2	powder	11
	0.97	10^{19} (15°)	50	film	12
	0.86	5×10^{15} (25°)	10^2	powder	8
	1.3	—	2.1×10^5	powder	13
	0.85	10^{15} (15°)	2	film	12
pentacene	0.66	3.2×10^{12} (50°)	—	powder	14
	0.75	10^{14} (15°)	10	film	12
	0.58	2.4×10^9 (50°)	—	powder	14
hexacene	0.57	3.8×10^{10} (50°)	—	powder	14
biphenyl	1.46	1.7×10^{15} (50°)	—	powder	15

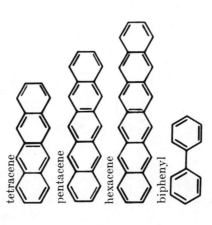

Table 4-1. The Electrical Resistivity and Energy Gaps of Monomeric Organic Compounds. (*continued*)

Substance and Structure	E, eV	ρ ohm-cm	ρ_0 ohm-cm	Comments	Ref.
p-terphenyl	0.6	10^{14} (25°)	—	single crystal	16
	1.06	5×10^{14} (50°)	—	powder	15
p-quaterphenyl	0.89	1.0×10^{15} (50°)	—	powder	15
p-quinquiphenyl	0.91	2.0×10^{15} (50°)	—	powder	15
p-sexiphenyl	0.91	7.0×10^{14} (50°)	—	powder	15
trans-stilbene	0.91			single crystal	17
4-phenyl stilbene(trans)	0.86			single crystal	17
4,4'-diphenyl stilbene (*trans*)	0.80			single crystal	17

compound					ref
fluorene				powder	
acenaphthene	1.0		9	powder	13
phenanthrene	0.65		6×10^4	powder	13
1,2-benzanthracene	1.04	10^{16} (30°)	—	powder	18
pyrene	1.2	10^{20} (15°)	10^{-3}	single crystal a-b plane	10
	1.0	5×10^{17} (15°)	1	film	12
perylene	1.0	4×10^{18} (15°)	—	powder	19
	1.1	10^{13} (15°)	—	film	19
	1.0	10^{18} (15°)	—	surface cell film one or two micron thick, sandwich cell	19

Table 4-1. The Electrical Resistivity and Energy Gaps of Monomeric Organic Compounds. (continued)

Substance and Structure	E, eV	ρ ohm-cm	ρ_0 ohm-cm	Comments	Ref.
chrysene	1.05	6.5×10^{15} (15°)	—	single crystal perpendicular to plane	20
	1.1	4.1×10^{13} (15°)	—	single crystal parallel to plane	20
	1.1	4×10^{19} (15°)	10^2	film	12
	1.5		0.27	powder	13
anthanthrene	0.84	1.5×10^{19} (15°)	3.4×10^4	powder	12
coronene	1.15	1.7×10^{17} (15°)	5	powder	11
	0.85	$10^{12} \sim 10^{13}$ (15°)		powder	19
	0.83			film, surface type cell	19
	0.80	$10^{17} \sim 10^{18}$ (15°)		film	19
				sandwich cell	19
meso-naphtho-dianthracene	0.6	4.0×10^{18} (15°)	1.8×10^8	powder	21

 0.51	4.5×10^{16} (15°)	2.0×10^7	powder	21
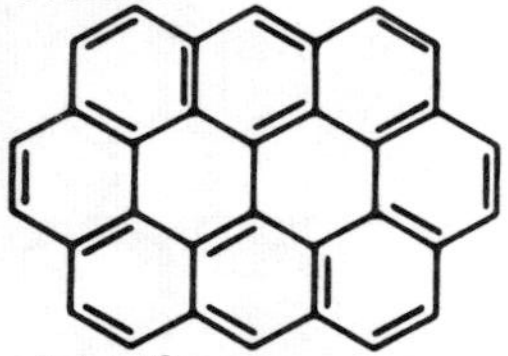 0.55	2.3×10^{15} (15°)	3.1×10^5	powder	21
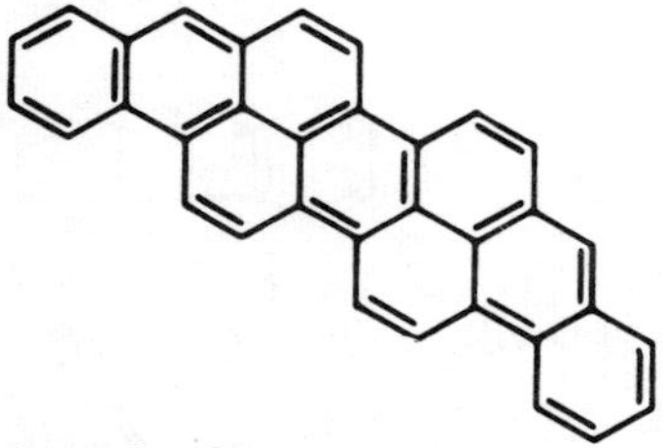 0.43	2.1×10^{14} (15°)		powder	19
0.45	10^9 (15°)		film surface cell	19
0.45	10^{14} (15°)		film sandwich cell	19
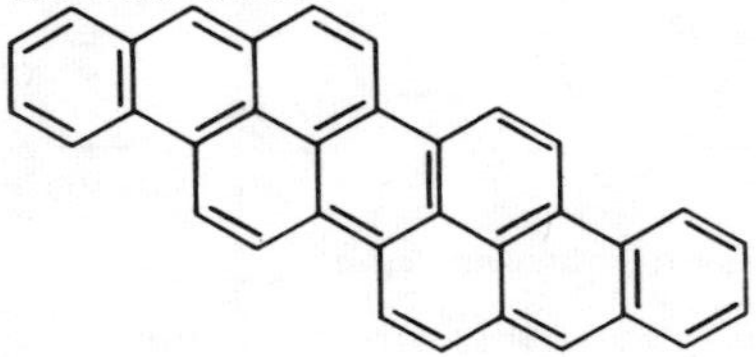 0.41	2.1×10^{14} (15°)	6.9×10^6	powder	21
0.81	3.6×10^{14} (20°)	20	powder	22

pyranthrene

ovalene

violanthrene

isoviolanthrene

Table 4-1. The Electrical Resistivity and Energy Gaps of Monomeric Organic Compounds. (continued)

Substance and Structure	E, eV	ρ ohm-cm	ρ_0 ohm-cm	Comments	Ref.
quaterrylene	0.3	10^{13} (15°)		single crystal perpendicular to a-b plane	23
	0.3	10^5 (15°)		single crystal parallel to a-b plane	23
2. Aromatic compounds with quinone structure					
9-fluorene	1.4		6.3×10^{-11}		13
o-chloranil	1.5	10^{15} (25°)	—	powder	24
anthanthrone	0.85	7.7×10^{18} (15°)	9.7×10^3	powder	21

5,6-N-pyridine 1,9-benzanthrone	1.60	8.5×10^{22} (15°)	1.4×10^{-5}	powder	25
isoviolanthone	0.38	5.7×10^{9} (15°)	1.5×10^{3}	powder	26
	0.68	3.2×10^{14} (20°)	5.2×10^{2}	powder	22
flananthrone	0.35	1.4×10^{11} (15°)	9.5×10^{4}	powder	25

Table 4-1. The Electrical Resistivity and Energy Gaps of Monomeric Organic Compounds. (continued)

Substance and Structure	E, eV	ρ ohm-cm	ρ_0 ohm-cm	Comments	Ref.
pyranthrone	0.51	3.9×10^{15} (15°)	3.7×10^{6}	powder	26
	0.9		1.3×10^{-1}	powder	13
indanthrone	0.32	7.5×10^{14} (15°)	2.5×10^{9}	powder	25
	0.33		1.8×10^{-1}	powder	13
violanthone	0.39	2.3×10^{10} (15°)	2.9×10^{3}	powder	26

meso-naphthodianthrone 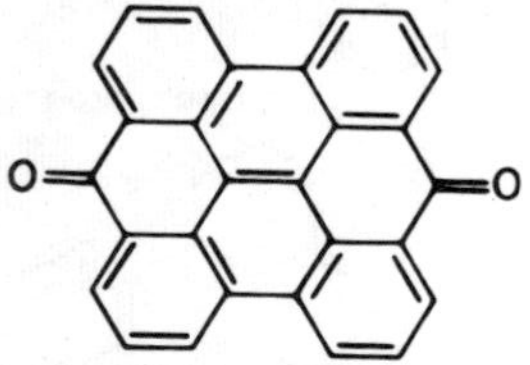	0.65	1.5×10^{18} (15°)	6.0×10^{6}	powder	21
indanthrone black 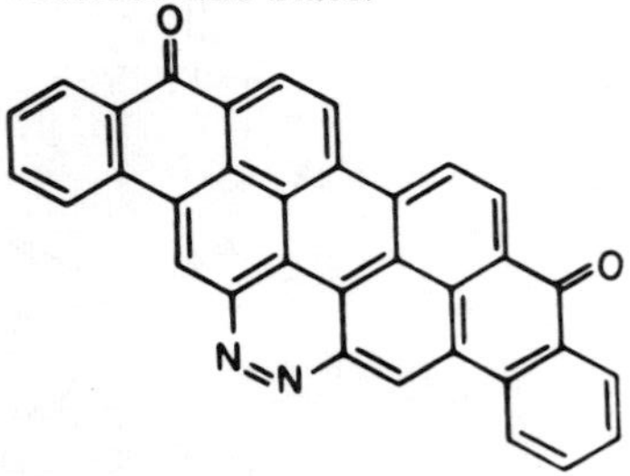	0.28	2.5×10^{8}	3.5×10^{3}	powder	25
cyananthrone 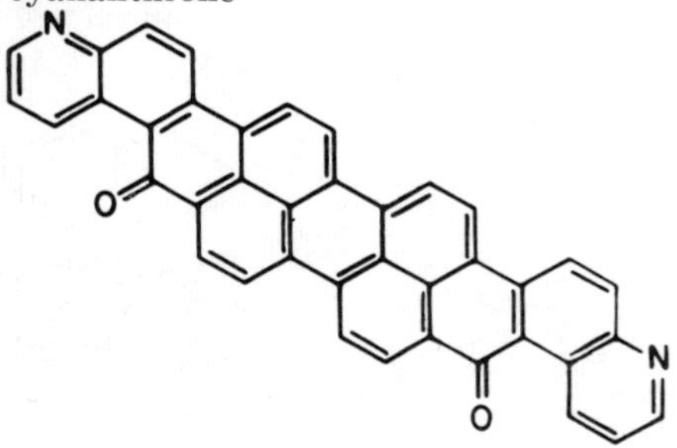	0.10	1.2×10^{7}	2.2×10^{5}	powder	25

meso-naphthodianthrone

indanthrone black

cyananthrone

Table 4-1. The Electrical Resistivity and Energy Gaps of Monomeric Organic Compounds. (continued)

3. Aromatic compounds containing nitrogen atom

Substance and Structure	E, eV	ρ ohm-cm	ρ_0 ohm-cm	Comments	Ref.
imidazol	1.3	10^{11} (25°)		powder	27
benzimidazole	1.5 ~ 2.0	10^{15} (25°)		> 100°C powder	27
	0.8 ~ 1.2			50 ~ 100°C powder	27
phenazine	1.1			zone refined material, powder	27
	1.9 ~ 2.0			sublimed material	27
acridine	0.33		3×10^7	powder	13
1,9,4,10-anthra-dipyrimidine	1.6	8.8×10^{24} (15°)	1.3×10^{-3}	powder	25
3,4-benzacridine	1.2	10^{15} (30°)		powder	18

1,2-benzacridine	1.05	10^{17} (30°)		powder	18
2,3-benzacridine	0.83	10^{17} (30°)		powder	18
indanthrazine	0.33	1.4×10^{15} (15°)	2.2×10^{9}	powder	18
4. *Naphthalene derivative*					
2-methoxynaphthalene	3.0		3×10^{-38}	powder	7
1-naphthylamine	1.5		5.6×10^{-14}	cooling cycle powder	7
	2.2		7.6×10^{-8}	heating cycle powder	7
1-nitrophthalene	1.2		6.0×10^{-6}	powder	7

Table 4-1. The Electrical Resistivity and Energy Gaps of Monomeric Organic Compounds. (*continued*)

Substance and Structure	E, eV	ρ ohm-cm	ρ_0 ohm-cm	Comments	Ref.
5. *Phthalocyanines*					
a. metal free	0.75			powder, β form measured by radio-frequency technique	1
	0.85			single crystal perpendicular to (010) plane also parallel to (010) plane	28
	0.7 ~ 0.9			parallel to b axis	29
	0.45			powder	30
b. copper	0.9		2.6×10^4	powder	31
	1.04			powder	11
	0.82		7.4×10^{-3}	single crystal perpendicular to (010) plane	28
	0.93			single crystal parallel to b axis	29
	0.40			powder in oxygen	30
	0.60			powder in vacuum	30
c. platinum	1.76		4.4×10^3	powder	31
d. cobalt	0.8			single crystal perpendicular to (010) plane	28

Compound			Condition	Ref.
			single crystal perpendicular to (010) plane	28
f. magnesium	0.40		powder in vacuum	30
	0.25		powder in oxygen	30
6. Free radicals				
αα'-diphenyl β-picryl-hydrazyl (DPPH) radical	0.13	10^{-6}	powder measured by AC method	1
	0.75		powder measured by DC method	1
	0.08	10^{-8}	film measured by AC method	32
	0.18	10^{-7}	film measured by DC method	32
	0.7	5.6×10^{-1}	powder	7
	0.73	10^{-1}	DC method	33

2,6,3'5' tetra t-butyl 4'-phenoxy 4-methylene 2,5-cyclohexadiene-1 radical (Coppinger's radical)

Compound				
1,3-dimethyl-1 (phenylimine oxide) butylidene-3, N'-phenyl N'-oxynitrogen radical (Banfield and Kenyon's radical)	1.15	10^{5}	powder DC method	33

Table 4-1. The Electrical Resistivity and Energy Gaps of Monomeric Organic Compounds. (continued)

Substance and Structure		E, eV	ρ ohm-cm	ρ_0 ohm-cm	Comments	Ref.
7. Dyestuffs						
crystal violet	chloride	0.36	10^{10} (20°)		film	34
	sulfate	0.28			powder	35
	oxalate				powder	35
indigo		0.9	10^{13} (20°)		film	34
fluorecein-Na		1.0	10^{13} (20°)		film	34
fuchsine		0.92			film	34

malachite green

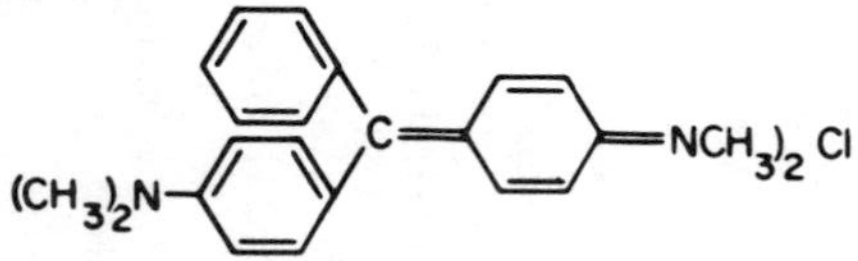

film 0.77 36

8. *Miscellaneous*

hydroquinone

under 130°
α form 1.1 37

above 130°
β form 2.1 37

ferrocene

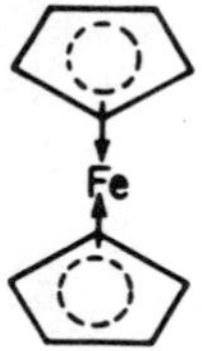

powder 0.65 0.78 13

References

1. Eley, D. D., and Parfitt, G. D., *Trans. Faraday Soc.*, 1529 (1955).
2. Kronick, P. L., Abstracts on "Organic Crystal Symposium," Ottawa, October, 1962.
3. Inokuchi, H., *Bull. Chem. Soc. Japan*, **27**, 22 (1954).
4. Forster, E. O., Abstract on "Organic Crystal Symposium," Ottawa, October, 1962.
5. Pick, H., and Wissman, W., Z. *Physik*, **138**, 436 (1954).
6. Riehl, N., *Ann. Physik* [6], **20**, 93 (1957).
7. Brown, G. P., and Aftergut, S., Proc. of the Princeton University Conference on Semiconduction in Molecular Solids, Princeton, New Jersey, 1960.
8. Okamoto, Y., Huang, F. T., Gordon, A., Brenner, W., and Rubin, B., "Organic Semiconductors," Ed. J. J. Brophy and J. W. Buttery, The Macmillan Co., New York, 1962.
9. Mette, H., and Pick, H., Z. *Physik.*, **134**, 566 (1953).
10. Inokuchi, H., *Bull. Chem. Soc. Japan*, **29**, 131 (1956).
11. Eley, D. D., Parfitt, G. D., Perry, M. J., and Taysum, D. H., *Trans. Faraday Soc.*, **49**, 79 (1953).
12. Northrop, D. C., and Simpson, O., *Proc. Roy Soc.*, **A234**, 124 (1956).
13. Rust, J. B., Haak, F. A., and Nolta, J. P., WADD Technical Report (U.S. Air Force), 60-111, June (1960).
14. Okamoto, Y., and Gordon, A., unpublished results.
15. Okamoto, Y., and Huang, F. T., unpublished results.
16. Hill, D. E., and Goldsmith, G. J., *Phys. Rev.*, **98**, 238 (1955).
17. Drehfahl, G., and Henkel, H. J., Z. *Phys. Chem.*, (Leipzig), **206**, 93 (1956).
18. Martin, G. C., and Ubbelohle, A. R., *J. Chem. Soc.*, 4948 (1961).
19. Inokuchi, H., Kuroda, H., and Akamatu, H., *Bull. Chem. Soc., Japan*, **34**, 749 (1961).
20. Sano, M., and Akamatu, H., *Bull. Chem. Soc., Japan*, **34**, 1569 (1961).
21. Inokuchi, H., *Bull. Chem. Soc., Japan*, **24**, 222 (1951).
22. Parkyns, N. D., and Ubbelohde, A. R., *J. Chem. Soc.*, **2110** (1961).
23. Inokuchi, H., Harada, Y., and Maruyama, Y., Abstracts on "Organic Crystal Symposium," Ottawa, October, 1962.
24. Kearns, D. R., and Calvin, M., *J. Am. Chem. Soc.*, **83**, 2110 (1961).
25. Inokuchi, H., *Bull. Chem. Soc., Japan*, **25**, 28 (1952).
26. Akamatu, H., and Inokuchi, H., *J. Chem. Phys.*, **18**, 810 (1950).
27. Aftergut, S., and Brown, G. P., "Organic Semiconductors," Ed. J. J. Brophy and J. W. Buttrey, p. 79, The Macmillan Co., New York, 1962.
28. Fielding, P. E., and Gutman, F., *J. Chem. Phys.*, **26**, 411 (1957).
29. Kleitman, D., U.S. Technical Services Report, PS 111419, August (1953).
30. Vartanyan, A. T., *J. Phys. Chem. (U.S.S.R.)* **22**, 769 (1948).
31. Felmeyer, W., and Wolf, I., *J. Electro. Chem. Soc.*, 141 (March, 1958).
32. Eley, D. D., and Inokuchi, H., Z. *Electro. Chem.*, **63**, 29 (1959).
33. Eley, D. D., and Wills, M. R., "Symposium on Electrical Conductivity in Organic Solids," Ed. H. Kallmann and M. Silver, p. 257, Interscience Publishers, New York, 1961.
34. Terenin, A., *Proc. Chem. Soc.*, 321 (1961).
35. Nelson, R. C., *J. Chem. Phys.*, **20**, 1327 (1952).
36. Meier, H., Z. *Phys. Chem.*, (Leipzig) **208**, 340 (1958).
37. Pignon, K., *Poczniki Chem.*, **29**, 939 (1955); *C. A.* 6112 (1956).

5

Charge-Transfer Complexes

Charge transfer complexes have been defined as being formed from the interaction of a wide variety of molecules, primarily aromatics, which can behave as electron donors (D) with electron acceptors (A), of various structures including quinones, nitro compounds, halogens, etc. The character of these complexes has been considered in terms of quantum theory by Mulliken[1] whose concepts were recently reviewed by McGlynn.[2]

The ground state of a 1:1 complex can be described by the wave function ψ, given by

$$\psi = a\psi_0(A:D) + b\psi_1(A^-:D^+)$$

where ψ_0 denotes the nonbonding wave function, such as the van der Waals type, and ψ_1 is the dative bonding wave function, corresponding to a structure of the complex in which an electron is transferred from the donor (D) to the acceptor (A). The combination of the two wave functions leads to a gain in energy (resonance energy). According to Mulliken, the attractive force arises from such a resonance as the intermolecular charge transfer force. The molecular addition compounds may be formed as a result of this charge transfer interaction between components, such as the aromatic hydrocarbon molecules being the electron donors and the halogen molecules the acceptors. The formation of charge transfer complexes is accompanied by characteristic spectral bands associated with the transition from the no-bond to the dative bond state, and most of the studies of these systems have been concerned with the spectral and solution properties rather than solid state properties.

The solid state structures of these complexes have not yet been clarified. However, Hassel[3] has succeeded in determining the crystal structure of the 1:1 benzene-bromine complex at −40 to −50°C. The bromine atoms were found to be symmetrically located on the common chief axis of two neighboring benzene rings. The crystal was built up of chains consisting of alternating benzene and bromine molecules. No change in the Br-Br distances (2.36 A) was found. Harding and Wallwork[4] considered the crystal structure of the chloranil-hexamethyl benzene complex to have a zig-zag arrangement in which one-half of the chloranil molecule interacts strongly with the molecule below.

Additional evidence for orbital interaction between electron donor and electron acceptor molecules in crystal can be found in Nakamoto's study of the polarizability.[5] In crystals of aromatic hydrocarbons, the density distribution of the π electrons is larger in the direction parallel to the planes, while in the complexes the density distribution is greater perpendicular to the planes.

A voluminous literature is rapidly being built up on investigation relating to the preparation and electrical properties of various kinds of charge-transfer complexes. Resistivity measurements have been reported on a wide variety of complexes; and, in general, a lowering of electrical resistivity has been associated with complex formation. The more significant investigations are discussed below.

Aromatic Hydrocarbon-Halogen Complexes

Polycyclic aromatic hydrocarbons generally form complexes with halogens, particularly bromine and iodine. When bromine is used to form complexes with aromatic compounds, a substitution reaction on the aromatic rings occurs with simultaneous liberation of hydrogen bromide. These complexes are only stable at very low temperatures. The composition of certain aromatic compound-iodine complexes has been determined quite accurately. The system perylene-iodine, for example, forms two different complexes, e.g., $C_{20}H_{12}:1.5:I_2$ and $C_{20}H_{12}:3\ I_2$.[6] The composition of the violanthrene-iodine complex is believed to be nonstoichiometric. Generally, the complexes have compositions such that one hydrocarbon molecule complexes with between one and a half to four halogen molecules, depending on the molecular size of the aromatics.[7]

The first important investigation of the lowering of the electrical resistivity of these aromatic hydrocarbon-halogen complexes was reported by Akamatu, Inokuchi, and Matsunaga as early as 1954. This property as well as the usual temperature dependence on conductivity qualify these complexes for consideration as organic semiconductors.[8,9] The data are shown in Table 5-1.

Table 5-1. Semiconductive Data of Aromatic Hydrocarbon-halogen Charge Transfer Complexes.

Addition Compound	Mole Ratio	$\rho_{15}°C$ ohm-cm	E, eV	Spin Population per One Hydrocarbon Molecule
Perylene-bromine	1:2	7.8	0.065	—
Perylene-iodine	1:1.5	10.0	0.03	0.06
Pyranthrene-iodine	1:2	17	0.045	0.09
Violanthrene-bromine	1:2	66	0.10	—
Violanthrene-iodine	1:2	45	0.075	0.14
Perylene-iodine[a]	2:3		0.019	
Pyrene-iodine[a]	1:2		0.14 (> 200°K)	
			0.068 (< 200°K)	

[a] From Ref. 6.

The electrical resistivity of the violanthrene-iodine[7,10] and perylene-iodine[11] complexes is a function of the iodine content. It first decreases with increase of the iodine content and then increases again after going through a minimum. The minimum value is 45 ohm-cm. The E for this low resistivity composition is 0.075 eV. The data are shown in Figure 5-1.

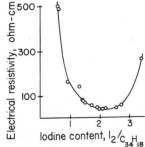

Figure 5-1. Electrical resistivity of violanthrene-iodine system as a function of iodine content.

A similar coronene-iodine complex has been studied by Labes, et al.[12] This system is rather stable chemically. The analysis and specific resistivities of a number of samples are shown in Table 5-2.

Table 5-2. Analysis and Resistivities of Various Coronene-Iodine Complexes.

% Iodine[a]	Method of Preparation, moles Coronene/moles Iodine	Resistivity ρ, ohm-cm room temperature	E, eV
45.9, 44.8	1:5[b]	1.2×10^{10}	0.31[c]
47.2, 47.5	1:10	2.3×10^{8}	—
47.3, 47.7	1:30	3.8×10^{8}	—
45.5	1:10	1.9×10^{9}	0.28
46.3	1:10	1.8×10^{9}	0.30

[a] Theoretical per cent iodine for 1:1 complex = 45.8.
[b] Individual compounds dissolved in hot s-tetrachloroethane, mixed, and allowed to cool.
[c] Value measured one month after preparation of complex.

Various other iodine complexes are being experimentally investigated. Thus, β-carotene-triiodine[13] and indole-iodine[14] complexes were reported. Their energy gaps were measured as $E = 0.55$ ($\rho_{25}° = 2 \times 10^{10}$ ohm-cm) and $E = 0.11$ eV, respectively. Isoviolanthrene and isoviolanthrone complexes with monoiodine chloride were prepared.[20] The conductance parameters are shown in Table 5-3.

Aromatic Hydrocarbon-Metal Halide Complexes

The formation of highly colored solids from the reaction of aromatic hydrocarbons with metal halides such as antimony pentachloride and tin tetrachloride was noted more than a half century ago by Mayer[15] and other investigators.[16,17,18] The electrical properties of these complexes were not determined. Recently Blomgren and Kommandeur prepared a stable complex of perylene and antimony pentachloride and measured the conductivity and also the conductivity temperature relationship.[19] Activation energies were found to be in the order of 0.067 to 0.098 eV. In general the behavior of this complex was quite similar to that exhibited by the previously studied perylene-iodine one.

Complexes of isoviolanthrene and isoviolanthrone with aluminum chloride and titanium chloride were prepared.[20] The titanium complexes were found to exhibit a higher conductance than the aluminium complexes. These results are shown in Table 5-3.

Table 5-3. Electronic Properties of Addition Complexes of Isoviolanthrene and Isoviolanthrone.

Donor	Acceptor	Ratio D/A	$\rho_{20}°C$	ρ_0	E, eV
Isoviolanthrone			3.2×10^{14}	520	0.68
"	$AlCl_3$	1/3.7	2.6×10^{12}	13	0.65
"	$TiCl_4$	1/1.87	3.0×10^{10}	0.69	0.64
"	ICl	1/3.73	1.1×10^9	1.9	0.49
"	ICl	1/1.90	2.2×10^8	15	0.47
"	ICl	1/1.45	4.5×10^{11}	7.1	0.62
"			3.6×10^{14}	20	0.81
Isoviolanthrene	$AlCl_3$	1/3.2	36	0.7	0.11
"	$TiCl_4$	1/1.29	354	2.6	0.13
"	I	1/1.52	580	7.6	0.11
"	K	1/4	100	3.7	0.083
"	Na	1/2.37	61	10	0.048

Aromatic Hydrocarbon-Metal Complexes

Aromatic hydrocarbons also form complexes with certain alkali metals. The evaporation of an aromatic hydrocarbon film such as naphthalene or anthracene onto a sodium or potassium film has been noted to increase the efficiency of photoelectric emission of the alkali metal.[21,22] This has been taken as indicative of complex formation between the metal and the anthracene, particularly in view of the observed spectral characteristics of this phenomenon.

The solid complexes of anthracene with lithium, potassium and sodium metals were investigated by Ubbelohde and his associates.[23,24,25] Typical preparations consisted of introducing an excess of alkali metal into an organic solvent containing a predetermined quantity of anthracene. The color of the solid complexes ranged from yellow for lithium to red-brown for sodium and gray for potassium. The empirical formula of the solid complex M_xAn is the range between $x = 0$ and $x = 2$. The hydrocarbon acts as the electron acceptor in the formation of these complexes which have been shown to exhibit paramagnetic behavior.

The conductivity characteristics of these metal-anthracene complexes are shown in Table 5-4.

Table 5-4. The Semiconductive Data of the Alkali Metal-Anthracene Complex.

Complex	$\sigma_{20}°C$, ohm^{-1} cm^{-1}	E, eV
Na$_{1.42}$:An*	3.51×10^{-10}	0.58
Na$_{2.08}$:An	1.6×10^{-9}	0.35
Na$_{2.12}$:An	5×10^{-9}	0.33
Li$_{1.16}$:An	7.73×10^{-12} (80°C)	0.66
K$_{1.18}$:An	6.38×10^{-12}	0.55

* An—Anthracene.

It has been found that the conductivity of the anthracene-alkali metal complexes depends on the metal content of the complex. It increases as the metal content becomes greater.

The preparation of complexes of 1,2-benzanthracene and 1,2-benzacridine with sodium has been reported.[26] They were found to have higher conductivities than analogous iodine complexes. Typical data are given in Table 5-5.

Table 5-5. Conductance Parameter of Aromatic Complexes with Iodine or Sodium at 30°C.

Donor	Acceptor	Ratio (D/A)	$\sigma \times 10^{-12}$, ohm^{-1} cm^{-1}	E, eV
1,2-Benzanthracene	I$_2$	1/1.74	1.0	0.90
	Na	1/1.02	110	0.66
1,2-Benzacridine	I$_2$	1/2.0	0.018	1.4
	Na	1/1.99	90	0.50

Aromatic Hydrocarbon—Nitro compound Complexes

The preparation of complexes from aromatic hydrocarbons and picric acid was carried out long ago. Such complexes were employed for the identification of hydrocarbons. The electrical resistivities of complexes formed between various aromatics and trinitrobenzene were studied by Kuroda, Yoshihara, and Akamatu[27] and are shown in Table 5-6.

Table 5-6. Electrical Resistivities of Trinitrobenzene-Complexes.

Donor	ρ_0	$\rho_{15}°$	E, eV
Anthracene	3×10	9×10^{17}	0.45
Phenanthrene	1×10^{-4}	7×10^{18}	0.62
Pyrene	2	1×10^{20}	0.55
Chrysene	2×10^{-3}	7×10^{18}	0.60
Perylene	5×10^3	1×10^{19}	0.42
Anthanthrene	2×10^2	1×10^{18}	0.43
Violanthrene	2×10^3	5×10^{13}	0.29
N,N,N,N'-Tetramethylbenzidine	2×10^2	1×10^{17}	0.41
Aniline	4×10^{-7}	1×10^{17}	0.64
p-Phenylenediamine	2×10^2	8×10^{16}	0.50
p-Chloroaniline	5×10^{12}	5×10^{13}	0.68
N,N-Dimethylaniline	7×10^{-4}	1×10^{16}	0.50
α-Naphthylamine	1×10^{-4}	3×10^{17}	0.59

Semi-quinone Type Molecular Complexes

The ability of quinones to form stable solid complexes with aromatic amines has been known for many decades.[28] Complex formation is now attributed to interaction of the electron poor system of the quinone with the electron rich amine component.

Some of the solid complexes formed between aromatic diamines and relatively strong Lewis acids, such as polyhaloquinones, exhibit electron paramagnetic resonance absorption, indicating presence of unpairing of electron spins.[29,30]

Eley, et al., have investigated the semiconductivity of charge transfer complexes between halogenated quinones and aromatic amines.[31] Typical charge transfer complexes which were studied included chloranil-N,N-dimethylaniline, bromanil-N,N-dimethylaniline, iodanil-N,N-dimethylaniline, etc. Resistivity measurements were made on compressed powder samples using both a-c and d-c methods as shown in Table 5-7.

Labes, et al., have undertaken the investigation of similar charge transfer complexes. Data on such complexes are summarized in Table 5-8.[12]

Seebeck coefficients were measured on the chloranil 3,8-diaminopyrene complex. It was synthesized by mixing the compounds separately dissolved in hot xylene in a 1:1 molar ratio. The Seebeck coefficients are quite low and increase with decreasing

Table 5-7. Organic Semiconductor Data for Semi-quinone Type Complexes.

Complexes	ρ, ohm-cm, d-c Method, 22°	ρ, ohm-cm, a-c Method, 22°	Energy Gap E
Chloranil N,N-dimethylaniline	8.1×10^8	5×10^7	0.24
Bromanil N,N-dimethylaniline	1.5×10^9	9×10^7	0.23
Iodanil N,N-dimethylaniline	1.7×10^8	3×10^7	0.22
Chloranil N,N,N',N'-tetramethyl p-phenylene diamine	2.0×10^4	1.3×10^4	0.27
Bromanil N,N,N',N'-tetramethyl p-phenylene diamine	1.3×10^5	4.2×10^4	0.28
Iodanil N,N,N',N'-tetramethyl p-phenylene diamine	1.5×10^6	1.1×10^5	0.30

Table 5-8. Room Temperature Electrical Resistivities of Molecular Complexes.

Acceptor	Donor	Resistivity ρ, ohm-cm, room temperature
Chloranil	Pyrene	10^{11}
"	Perylene	10^8
"	Hexamethylbenzene	10^{11}
"	N,N-Dimethylaniline	10^{10}
"	p-Phenylenediamine	10^7
"	1,5-Diaminonaphthalene	10^{11}
"	1,8-Diaminonaphthalene	10^{11}
"	p-Aminodiphenylamine	10^{10}
"	Tetramethyl-p-phenylenediamine	10^9
"	3,8-Diaminopyrene	10^4
"	3,10-Diaminopyrene	10^6
"	p-Anisidine	10^{11}
Bromanil	p-Phenylenediamine	10^{10}
"	3,8-Diaminopyrene	10^4
Iodanil	p-Phenylenediamine	10^{11}
"	3,8-Diaminopyrene	10^6

temperature. The temperature dependence of the Seebeck coefficient of 3,8-diaminopyrene-chloranil is shown in Figure 5-2.

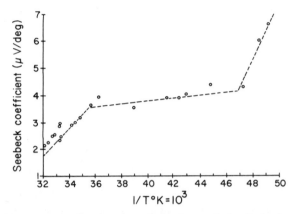

Figure 5-2. Temperature dependence of the Seebeck coefficient of 3,8-diaminopyrene-chloranil.

Single crystal complexes of 1,5-diaminonaphthalene, diaminodurene, and 1,6-diaminopyrene with chloranil have also been investigated. The resistivities of these complexes in the three crystal directions are summarized in the following Table 5-9.[32]

Table 5-9. Resistivities of Charge Transfer Complexes of Chloranil.

Data	X	Single Crystal Y	Z	Micro-crystalline
		Diaminodurene-chloranil		
$\rho(25°)$, ohm-cm	7×10^4	6.9×10^4	8.4×10^4	3×10^4
E, eV	0.13			0.13
		1,5-Diaminonaphthalene-chloranil		
$\rho(25°)$, ohm-cm	1.3×10^9	6.3×10^{11}	2.0×10^{11}	7.2×10^{11}
E, eV	0.30	0.37	0.37	0.33
		1,6-Diaminopyrene-chloranil		
$\rho(25°)$, ohm-cm	10^5	10^6	10^9	4×10^3
E, eV		0.10		0.075

A large increase in the dark conductivity of metal free phthlocyanines was observed by Calvin, *et al.*, upon the addition of small amount of chloranil.[33,34] A comparison of the maximum values of the conductivity of chloranil doped phthalocyanine and pure metal free phthalocyanines are shown in Table 5-10.

Table 5-10. Dark Conductivities of Chloranil Doped and
Pure Metal Free Pathalocyanines.

| Temperature, °C | Resistivity, ohm-cm. | |
	Pure Metal Free	Chloranil Doped
25	10^3	10^{10}
−100	10^{-7}	10^7

These data have been explained on the basis that chloranil is
a strong electron acceptor and could, therefore, be expected to remove electrons from phthalocyanines. A large electron spin resonance absorption corresponding to the presence of unpaired electrons was observed with this system. The strength of the ESR
signal was found to be proportional to the amount of chloranil
added. It has been suggested that positive holes are formed in the
phthalocyanine layer as a result of this electron transfer and that
these holes give rise to the large dark current.

Kearns and Calvin have investigated the electrical resistivity
characteristics of violanthrene as the donor with various acceptor
layers such as o-chloranil, iodine, tetracyanoethylene, etc.[35] The
addition of as little as 3.5×10^{-5} mole of o-chloranil in a violanthrene film causes the dark conductivity to increase by factor of
8×10^5 over that of pure film. The same addition of iodine was
found to produce a 4×10^5-fold increase. Tetracyanoethylene resulted in a 4×10^3-fold increase. Further studies along these lines
are of considerable interest for purposes of elucidating the effects
of charge transfer complex formation.

7,7,8,8-Tetracyanoquinodimethane (TCNQ) Complexes

A most interesting recent development concerns the synthesis
of a new group of surprisingly conductive charge transfer complexes based on tetracyanoquinodimethane by researchers of the
Du Pont Company.[36,37] The tetracyanoquinodimethane forms three
types of electrically conducting organic solids. Crystalline charge
transfer complexes are obtained by interaction with aromatic
hydrocarbons, amines, and polyhydric phenols. These complexes
maintain the TCNQ quinoid character and show resistivity as low
as 10^3 to 10^4 ohm-cm as well as very weak ESR absorption char-

acteristics. In addition, the transfer of an electron to tetracyano-quinodimethane results in the formation of the anion radical TCNQ $\div$ which in combination with a variety of cations can form two series of stable salt-like derivatives. The anion radical TCNQ $\div$ is represented by the resonance forms shown in Figure 5-3.

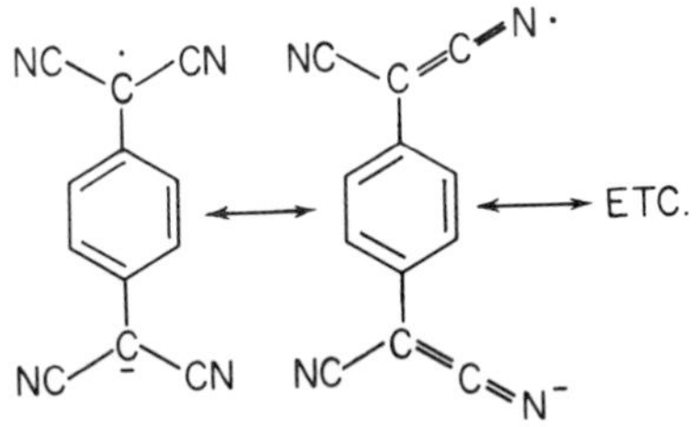

Figure 5-3

Salt-like compounds containing the TCNQ anion radical have been investigated in considerable detail. The chemical compositions of these derivatives are $M^+(TCNQ \div)(TCNQ°)$ respectively. It is considered that in both types of salt the band formed from the lowest normally unfilled molecular orbital of the TCNQ is partially filled: one half full for the first noted series of salts and one quarter full for the second. As a result of the rather weak intermolecular interactions characteristic of molecular crystals this band is quite narrow.[37] Both the band width and the exchange coupling of the electrons appear to be greatly influenced by the nature of the cation, M^+, and by whether or not $TCNQ°$ is present in the crystal.

The $M^+(TCNQ \div)$ salts in which M^+ may be a metallic or an organic cation show relatively high resistivities in the range of 10^4 to 10^{12} ohm-cm and weak ESR absorption in the solid state.[38] The second series of complexes, $M^+(TCNQ \div)(TCNQ°)$ have remarkably low resistivities, 10^{-2} to 10^3 ohm-cm, and variable ESR absorption characteristics.[38]

Complexs of TCNQ with many donor compounds are much less soluble than either of the components so that a large variety can be readily prepared by adding solutions of the donor compound to TCNQ in solvents such as tetrahydrofuran, chloroform, or dichloromethane. TCNQ anion-radical salt complexes are synthesized by the one-electron reduction with metal iodides or with certain metals;

$$MI + TCNQ \rightarrow M^+(TCNQ \cdot-) + \tfrac{1}{2}I_2$$
$$M^\circ + TCNQ \rightarrow M^+(TCNQ \cdot-)$$

The complexes, $M^+(TCNQ \cdot-)(TCNQ)^\circ$ are generally prepared by mixing the solution of alkyl or aryl substituted ammonium and oxonium TCNQ salts with neutral TCNQ. The characteristic black needles of the complexes are recrystallized from solvent such as acetonitrile.

The electronic properties of representative salts are shown in Tables 5-11, 5-12, and 5-13.

Table 5-11. π Complexes of TCNQ.[39]

Donor	Ratio (donor:TCNQ)	Resistivity, ohm-cm (room temp.)
p-Phenylenediamine	1:1	3×10^3 ($E = 0.28$ eV)
2-Methyl-p-phenylenediamine	1:1	3×10^5
N,N-Dimethyl p-phenylene diamine	1:1	2×10^9
N,N'-Dimethyl p-phenylenediamine	1:1	2×10^4
N,N,N',N'-Tetramethyl-p-phenylene-diamine	1:1	10^6
Diaminodurene	1:1	10^9
2,3-Diaminonaphthalene	1:1	10^{10}
1,5-Diaminonaphthalene	1:1	10^9
2-Aminofluorene	1:1	10^{10}
Anthracene	—	10^{11}
Pyrene	1:1	10^{12}
4,6,8-Trimethylazulene	1:1	10^9
Copper-8-quinolinolate	1:1	3×10^7
Copper chelate of pyrrole 2-aldyhydeimine	1:1	5×10^{10}
Nickel chelate of pyrrole 2-aldehydeimine	1:1	10^{11}

The quinolinium salts appear to have characteristics which permit the electrons of the TCNQ $\cdot-$ radicals to form conventional degenerate systems similar to metals. Conductivities are remarkably high, and the activation for conductivity is virtually absent. Electrical measurements on single crystals of these complex salts have demonstrated the marked anisotropy of resistivity relative to crystal axis.[39] Table 5-14 shows the typical results for this property.

Table 5-12. TCNQ $\bar{\ }$ Salts Containing Metal and Onium Cations.[39]

Complex	Resistivity, ohm-cm (room temp.)
Li$^+$ TCNQ $\bar{\ }$	2×10^5
Cs$^+$ TCNQ $\bar{\ }$	3×10^4 ($E = 0.15$ eV)
Na$^+$ TCNQ $\bar{\ }$	3×10^4
K$^+$ TCNQ $\bar{\ }$	5×10^3
(Cs$^+$)$_2$(TCNQ $\bar{\ }$)$_2$(TCNQ)	9×10^4 ($E = 0.36$ eV)
Ba^{++} (TCNQ $\bar{\ }$)$_2$	8×10^5
Cu$^+$ TCNQ $\bar{\ }$	2×10^2 ($E = 0.13$ eV)
Cu^{++} (TCNQ $\bar{\ }$)$_2$	2×10^2 ($E = 0.12$ eV)
Ag$^+$ TCNQ $\bar{\ }$	8×10^5
NH$_4$$^+$ TCNQ $\bar{\ }$	6×10^4
(C$_2$H$_5$)$_3$NH$^+$ TCNQ $\bar{\ }$	10^9
(C$_6$H$_5$)$_3$(CH$_3$)P$^+$ TCNQ $\bar{\ }$	4×10^{10}
(C$_5$H$_5$N)$^-$ TCNQ $\bar{\ }$	10^6
(N-Methylquinolium)$^+$ TCNQ $\bar{\ }$	10^7
(CH$_3$)$_3$NH$^+$ (TCNQ $\bar{\ }$)(TCNQ)	5×10^6
(C$_2$H$_5$)$_4$N$^+$(TCNQ $\bar{\ }$)(TCNQ)	2×10^4
(CH$_3$)$_2$(t-C$_4$H$_9$)N$\overset{+}{H}$(TCNQ $\bar{\ }$)(TCNQ)	9

Table 5-13. Complex Salts Containing Aromatic and Heterocyclic Cations. [a,39]

Cation	Resistivity, ohm-cm (room temp.)
4-Hydroxy-N-benzylanilinium	55 ($E = 0.075$ eV)
4-Amino-N,N-diethylanilinium	175 ($E = 0.09$ eV)
4-Amino-2,3,5,6-tetramethylanilinium	8 ($E = 0.08$ eV)
Pyridium	37
Quinolinium	0.5 ($E = 0.013$ eV)
N-(n-Propyl)quinolium	2
2,2'-Bipyridinium	0.5

[a] All of these complexes have the composition cation (TCNQ $\bar{\ }$) (TCNQ).

Table 5-14. Anistropic Properties of TCNQ Complexes.

	Complexes and Resistivity, ohm-cm		
Axis	Triethyl Ammonium (TCNQ) $\bar{\ }_2$	Methyl Triphenyl Phosphonium (TCNQ) $\bar{\ }_2$	room temperature N-(n-Propyl) quinolinium (TCNQ) $\bar{\ }_2$
a	0.25	60	0.5
b	20	600	6
c	1000	10^5	450

Biological Systems

The concept of electron transfer processes in biological systems was first advanced by Szent Györgyi in 1941.[40] The application of solid state physics to energy and electron transplant phenomena in biological systems has since then been applied to a variety of as yet unsolved problems.[41] Charge transfer processes permit the transfer of electrons from one substance to another without incurring major energy losses since they do not involve rearrangements in molecular structure. They also make possible the consideration of many substances in processes such as biological oxidation—substances which can donate but one electron and, since they do not affect electrodes, were previously not thought of in terms of redox agents. Charge transfer process can also cause relatively inactive molecules to acquire high reactivities.

The problem of ascertaining the existence of a charge-transfer complex in biological systems is often a complicated one. Two techniques which are being applied for this purpose are optical and magnetic methods. Many charge transfer complexes are high colored, and spectral studies are useful. Weak light induced charge transfer complexes have been detected by consideration of the relationship between frequency and ionization potential. Magnetic methods are also of value. Paramagnetic behavior can be established by the use of the magnetic balance or electron spin resonance measurement. Free radicals give sharp and high ESR signals extending over 10 to 50 gauss. Weak charge transfer complexes give little or no ESR signals. Dipole measurements have also been employed for the study of charge transfer in biological systems.

A simple system with biological implications is quinhydrone formed by mixing quinone and hydroquinone. Quinhydrone is obtained by the interaction of the weak donor hydroquinone with the strong acceptor quinone. No ESR signals are detectable.

Of greater interest is the charge transfer complex between riboflavin and serotonin (5-hydroxytryptamine) Figure 5-4. The electron transfer will take place from the indole to the vitamin. The transferred electron may come from the electron rich 5-hydroxytryptamine or from the lone electron pair of its nitrogen. Charge transfer complexes have been formed by freezing of solutions of these two components in presence of 1 per cent hydrochloric acid.[41]

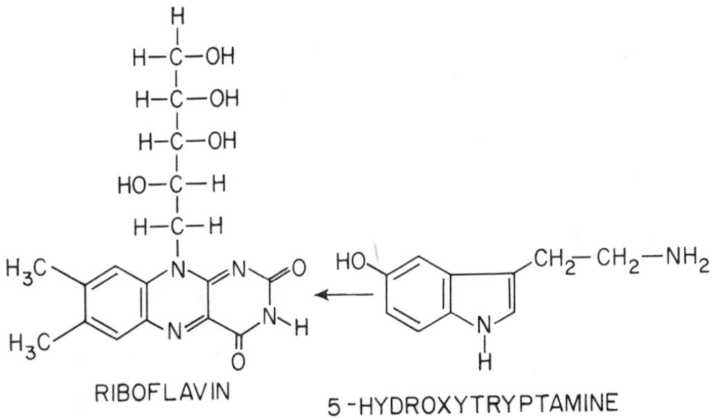

RIBOFLAVIN   5-HYDROXYTRYPTAMINE

Figure 5-4

Other donor-acceptor systems of biological importance have been discussed by Cilento and Giusti.[42] Freezing techniques have been employed to show electron transmission between serotinin and positively charged diphosphopyridine nuclolide (DPN). Charge transfer complexes with pteridines as an acceptor have been investigated by Fujimori.[43] The possible role of charge transfer in the function of DPN in biological oxidation was first suggested by Kosower.[44]

The cortisone-iodine system has been studied in considerable detail.[40] The iodine molecules act as an acceptor. Chloroform was used as a solvent for iodine in the preparation of this charge transfer complex. The spectroscopic data showed a broad absorption band with a maximum at 740 mμ where neither iodine nor the cortisone absorbed (Figure 5-5).

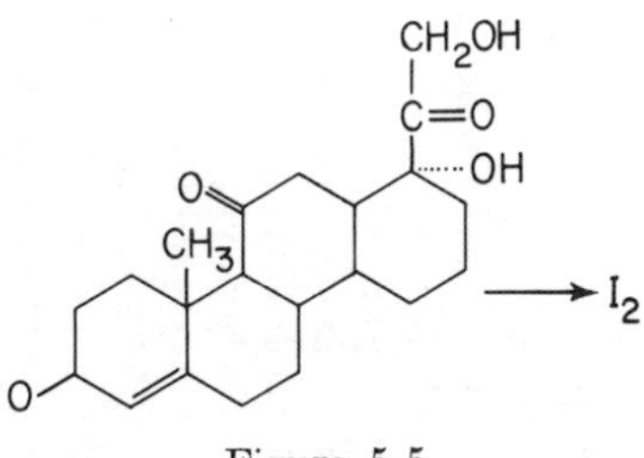

Figure 5-5

Table 5-15. Electronic Properties of Charge Transfer Complexes of Linear Polymers.

Complexes	Color of Complex	Energy Gap, eV	Conductivity 25°C, ohm^{-1} cm^{-1}	Polymer Used
Polyvinyl naphthalene			6.8×10^{-14}	
Polyvinyl mesitylene			1.1×10^{-13}	
Polystyrene			3.2×10^{-14}	
(Polyvinyl naphthalene)(tetracyanoethylene)[a]	dark green	0.60	3.2×10^{-15}	atactic form
(Polyvinyl naphthalene)$_2$(tetracyanoethylene)	"	0.55	7.4×10^{-15}	"
(Polyvinyl naphthalene)$_4$(tetracyanoethylene)	"	0.50	9.6×10^{-15}	"
(Polyvinyl naphthalene)(tetracyanoethylene)	"	0.60	2.8×10^{-15}	isotactic form
(Polyvinyl naphthalene)(chloranil)	dark brown	0.62	7.2×10^{-15}	atactic form
(Polyvinyl naphthalene)$_4$(chloranil)	"	0.50	1.6×10^{-14}	"
(Polyvinyl naphthalene)(chloranil)	"	0.36	1.1×10^{-14}	isotactic form
(Polyvinyl naphthalene)$_4$(chloranil)	"	0.39	1.3×10^{-14}	"
(Polyvinyl naphthalene)$_4$(2,3-dichloro 5,6-dicyano p-benzo quinone)	black	0.16	1.1×10^{-13}	atactic form
(Polyvinyl mesitylene)(tetracyanoethylene)	red brown	0.26	5.5×10^{-14}	"
(Poly acenaphthylene)$_4$(tetracyanoethylene)	green	0.33	3.7×10^{-15}	"

[a] Stoichiometry was described in terms of the molecular ratio of the number of aromatic units in the polymer chain to one molecule of acceptor.

Zaffaroni, *et al.* have described the color changes occurring from the interaction of steroids with iodine.[45] The probabilities are that charge transfer formation is involved by virtue of the strong donor ability of the ketosteroids.

The future progress of this field would appear to depend greatly on the development of more quantitative data on such charge transfer complexes with special emphasis on conductivity measurements and other means of characterization.

Charge Transfer Complexes with Linear Polymers

Data on the electronic properties of charge transfer complexes of linear polymers have recently been reported.[46] The polymeric electron donors were all of the vinyl type, i.e., polystyrene, polyvinyl naphthalene, polyacenaphthylene, and polyvinyl mesitylene. Electron acceptors were tetracyanoethylene, chloranil, and 2,3-dichloro-5,6-dicyano-*p*-benzoquinone. The charge transfer complexes were prepared by freeze drying methods. The required molecular amounts were dissolved together in benzene. The mixture was then frozen to 0°C and the benzene removed under high vacuum. The complexes are stable at elevated temperatures, some up to 130°C without decomposition.

Specific conductivity measurements were made using a vibrating reed electrometer at an applied d-c potential of 4.5 V under a pressure of 10 kg/cm². The conductivities of these complexes were generally not substantially higher than those of the linear polymeric electron donors. Slough explained the rather low conductivities in terms of lack of ordering of the π systems breaking the path of the charge carriers. The current carriers appear to be positively charged electron deficiencies (holes) based on Seebeck coefficient measurements. These are carried by aromatic π centers of the polymer chain and restriction of the orientation of these groups could lead to low mean free paths for the carriers. Typical data are summarized in Table 5-13.

References

1. Mulliken, R. S., *J. Am. Chem. Soc.*, **74**, 811 (1952); *J. Phys. chem.*, **56**, 801 (1952); *Rec. Trav. Chim.*, **75**, 845 (1956).
2. McGlynn, S. P., *Chem. Revs.*, **58**, 1113 (1958).
3. Hassel, O., *Mol. Phys.*, **1**, 241 (1958).

4. Harding, T. T., and Wallwork, S. C., *Acta Cryst.*, **8**, 787 (1955).
5. Nakamoto, K., *J. Am. Chem. Soc.*, **74**, 1739 (1952).
6. Kommandeur, and Hall, F. R., *J. Chem. Phys.*, **34**, 129 (1961).
7. Inokuchi, H., and Akamatu, H., "Solid State Physics," Vol. 12, New York, Academic Press, 1961.
8. Akamatu, H., Inokuchi, H., and Matsunaga, Y., *Nature.* **173**, 168 (1954).
9. Akamatu, H., Inokuchi, H., and Matsunaga, Y., *Bull. Chem. Soc. Japan*, **29**, 213 (1956).
10. Uchida, T., and Akamatu, H., *Bull. Chem. Soc. Japan.* **35**, 981 (1962).
11. Uchida, T., and Akamatu, H., *Bull. Chem. Soc. Japan.* **34**, 1015 (1961).
12. Labes, M. M., Sehr, R. A., and Bose, M., Proceedings of the Princeton University Conference on "Semiconductor in Molecular Solids," Princeton, N.J., 1960.
13. Huggins, C. M., and LeBlanc, O. H., *Nature.* **186**, 552 (1960).
14. Smaller, B., Isenberg, I., and Baird, S. L., *Nature.* **191**, 168 (1961).
15. Mayer, K. H., *Ber.*, **41**, 2568 (1908).
16. Hilpert, S., and Wolf, L., *Ber. deut. Chem. Gae*, **46**, 2215 (1913).
17. Brass, K., and Tengler, E., *Ber.*, **64**, 1650 (1931).
18. Brass, K., and Fanta, K., *Ber.*, **69**, 1 (1936).
19. Blomgren, G. E., and Kommandeur, I., *J. Chem. Phys.*, **35**, 1636 (1961).
20. Parkyns, N. D., and Ubbelohde, A. R., *J. Chem. Soc.*, 2110 (1961).
21. Suhrmann, R., *Z. Physik.*, **94**, 742 (1935).
22. Suhrmann, R., *Z. Physik.*, **111**, 18 (1937).
23. Holmes-Walker, W. A., and Ubbelohde, A. R., *J. Chem. Soc.*, 720 (1954).
24. Gracey, U. P. V., and Ubbelohde, A. R., *J. Chem. Soc.*, 4089 (1955).
25. Slough, W., and Ubbelohde, A. R., *J. Chem. Soc.*, 911, (1957); 918, (1957); 983, (1957).
26. Martin, G. C., and Ubbelohde, A. R., *J. Chem. Soc.*, 4948 (1961).
27. Kuroda, H., Yoshihara, K., and Akamatu, H., *Bull. Chem. Soc. Japan*, **35**, 1604 (1962).
28. Schlenk, W., *Ann.* **368**, 277 (1909).
29. Kainer, H., and Überle, A., *Chem. Ber.*, **88**, 1147 (1955).
30. Kainer, H., Bijl, D., and Rose-Innes, A. C., *Naturwiss*, **41**, 303 (1954). Bijl, D., Kainer, H., and Rose-Innes, A. C., *J. Chem. Phys.*, **30**, 765 (1959).
31. Eley, D. D., Inokuchi, H., and Willis, M. R., *Trans. Farad. Soc.*, 54 (1959).
32. Kronick, P. L., and Labes, M. M., "Organic Semiconductors," Ed. by J. J. Brophy and J. W. Buttrey, New York, The Macmillan Co., 1961.
33. Kearns, D., and Calvin, M., Bio-Organic Chemistry Quarterly Report, UCRL 8457 (September, 1958).
34. Kearns, D., Tollin, G., and Calvin, M., *J. Chem. Phys.*, **32**, 1020 (1960).
35. Kearns, D., and Calvin, M., *J. Am. Chem. Soc.*, **83**, 2110 (1961).
36. Kepler, R. G., Bierstedt, P. E., and Merrifield, R. E., *Phys. Rev. Letters*, **5**, 503 (1960).
37. Acker, D. S., Harder, R. J., Hertler, W. R., Mahler, W., Melby, L. R., Benson, R. E., and Mochel, W. E., *J. Am. Chem. Soc.*, **82**, 6408 (1960).
38. Chesnut, D. B., Foster, H., and Phillips, W. D., *J. Chem. Phys.*, **34**, 684 (1961).

39. Melby, L. R., Harder, R. J., Hertles, W. R., Mahler, W., Benson, R. E., and Mochel, W. E., *J. Am. Chem. Soc.*, **84**, 3374 (1962).
40. Geörgyi, A. Szent, *Science*, **93**, 609 (1941); see also *Nature* **148**, 157 (1941).
41. Geörgyi, A. Szent, "Introduction to Submolecular Biology," New York, Academic Press, 1960.
42. Cilento, G., and Gusti, P., *J. Am. Chem. Soc.*, **81**, 3901 (1959).
43. Fujimori, E., *Proc. Natl. Acad. Sci. U.S.*, **45**, 133 (1959).
44. Kosower, E. M., and Klinedinst, P. E., *J. Am. Chem. Soc.*, **78**, 3483 (1956).
45. Zaffaroni, A., Barton, R. B., and Keitman, E. H., *Sci.*, **111** 6 (1950).
46. Slough, W., *Trans. Faraday Soc.*, **58**, 2360 (1962).

6

Electronic Carbons

Alton F. Armington

The inclusion of a chapter on carbon in a book concerning organic semiconductors may appear strange to many readers, especially those who consider carbon an inorganic element. However, carbon can be regarded as a high molecular aromatic compound in view of its molecular structure as will be shown in this chapter. Thus, it might be expected the properties of this material should approximate the ultimate values of the polycyclic aromatic compound (naphthalene, anthracene, coronene, etc.) In addition, some of the properties of the molecular complex organic semiconductors (such as those with iodine) might be better understood through knowledge of the interstitial compounds of graphite which are crystalline in many instances. The same inference can be applied to the degraded polymer type of organic semiconductor, many of which can be represented as highly distorted and impure carbon structures. On the basis the relationship between organic semiconductors and carbon technology is quite apparent.

With the exception of carbon electrodes and resistors, electronic applications of carbon are still in the curiosity stage. Other uses of carbon date back thousands of years to prehistoric times when graphite was used as a drawing material, a use it still has today. Previous to 1900 graphite was, as it still is, used as a refractory material, principally in crucibles, because of its chemical inertness and high temperature stability.[1] Pyrocarbons and pyrographites which are newer materials also find their principal applications as refractories because of their thermal stability. A more familiar use of graphite, although extremely minute in terms of graphite consumption, is as a lubricant in applications where liquids cannot be used. Carbon black, an amorphous carbon, is used extensively as an absorbent of both gases and liquids. A considerable amount of this material is also used as a filler, particularly in the rubber industry. While this application is not new, a considerable amount of good research has been done on carbon blacks in the past few years, particularly in surface chemistry and related fields.[2]

Electrical uses of carbon, at the present time, are limited to application of its conductivity and the variation of its conductivity. Electrodes, primarily in the metallurgical industry, account for most of the carbon consumption in electrical applications. These electrodes are usually in the form of extruded rods of synthetic graphite. Brushes of molded graphite are also the result of the high conductivity of this material. Carbon resistors are fabricated by coating ceramic materials with organic material followed by a baking process to carbonize this coating. Impurities, specifically boron, can be added to this coating to alter the electrical properties.[3] In the older type resistors, a mixture of carbon and a less conductive material was encapsulated in an insulator through which two leads were passed.[1]

The applications discussed here are generally not the result of extensive research but have been developed more or less through an engineering approach. For this reason only a limited amount of carbon research was performed prior to World War II. Since then a considerable amount of work has been done both by the carbon industry and workers not connected with the industry. A large percentage of the workers are more concerned with the basic research of carbon particularly in the solid state field, than with product requirements. Some new uses of carbon have been found through this research, however. Pyrolytic graphite, mentioned previously, is an example of this.

General Properties of Carbon

There are two crystalline forms of carbon, namely graphite and diamond. The diamond form is characterized by tetrahedral covalent bonding between the carbon atoms with a bond distance of 1.54 A. While the diamond structure is not related to any of the organic semiconductor structures, certain modifications, which will be discussed in this chapter, show promise as high temperature semiconductors. In ideal graphite, carbon atoms are arranged in layers of fused hexagons with every other layer directly superimposed. The intermediate layers are also superimposed resulting in what is often referred to as an ABAB structure (Figure 6-1).

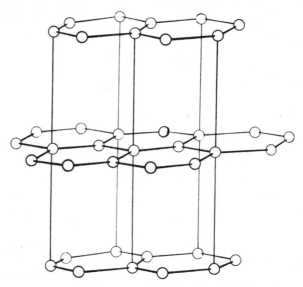

Figure 6-1. Model of ideal graphite. (Spacing between layer planes is 3.354 A.)

The bonding in graphite consists of three sigma bonds and a pi bond which is free to migrate within the molecule in a manner similar to that in organic solids.[4] A rhombohedral form of graphite has also been investigated in which every third layer is superimposed.[5] This form is metastable and reverts to the hexagonal form on heating to 1300°C. The rhombohedral form is usually produced by the mechanical working of graphite. In ideal graphite the layer carbons are 1.42 A apart while the layer distance is 3.354 A. Perfect graphite crystals are rarely produced synthetically and large crystals are not too prevalent in nature. Near ideal crystals have been found in upper New York and in

Ceylon.[1] However, most physical and chemical measurements are made on synthetic material which consists of partially oriented micro-crystallites. While these materials are satisfactory for the measurement of massive properties, such as X-ray analysis, much disagreement is found when more sensitive measurements are involved, as in the case of electronic properties or chemical kinetics.

Almost all properties of carbon, electronic included, are a function of the degree of crystal perfection in the sample. The degree of perfection varies, often uncontrollably, from near ideal to amorphous, which produces extensive variations in physical properties. Provided that the individual crystalline diameter exceeds a certain size (150 A), the degree of orientation is essentially a function of the heat treatment or graphitization temperature[6] as will be discussed in the next section. The crystalline perfection is also a function of the starting material,[7] impurities,[4] and the degree of orientation between crystallites. The degree of orientation within a crystallite can be estimated from X-ray results using the method of Franklin.[8] In this work Franklin takes the value of 3.354 for ideal graphite and 3.44 for a crystallite with no stacking order (Figure 6-2). Intermediate values are obtained by assuming four different orientations (and d-spacings) within the crystallite. This correlation is useful for characterizing the individual crystallites but is of little help when the orientation between the crystallites is being considered. The diameter of the crystallite varies from several thousand angstroms in natural graphite to less than one hundred angstroms for poorly aligned carbons. The degree of orientation between crystallites (in terms of having parallel basal planes) varies widely in synthetic materials, being random in carbon blacks and molded carbons but better than 99.9 per cent in the case of pyrolytic carbons.[9] It is obvious that this alignment can have a greater effect on the resulting properties of a carbon than the orientation within the crystallites.

The density of graphite calculated from X-ray measurements is 2.268.[4] This value is rarely found in practice due to the porosity of most carbon bodies as well as the micropore structure between crystallites. The larger d-spacing for less perfect graphites also can lower the density somewhat. Commercial pyrolytic graphite has a density of 2.20 with even higher densities reported in some cases.[9] Heat treated carbon blacks also have fairly high densities due to their low porosity although micropores are still present between the crystallites and the d-spacing is usually greater than 3.354 A. Densities as high as 2.1 have been reported for this type of carbon, but values closer to 1.5 are more common.[10] Graphite rods are porous and have a low density, even though the

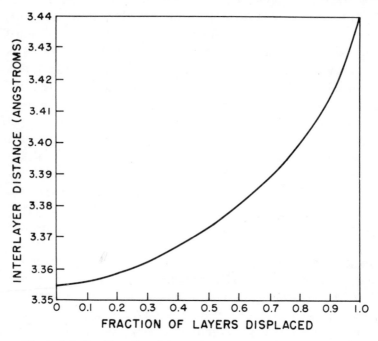

Figure 6-2. Stacking disorder as a function of interlayer distance.[8]

d-spacing is approximately that of natural graphite. The density of this material is usually 1.6 to 2.0.[11] It is often impregnated with coal tar pitch and regraphitized in order to improve the density and make a more impervious graphite. The density value reported here is the apparent density of the bulk material which includes open porosity of the sample. Helium densities are often reported which exclude the effects of open pores on density measurements.[10] This method usually produces densities about 0 to 10 per cent higher. The apparent density is used for comparison here since this is the density usually reported in the literature.

Thermal expansion and thermal conductivity are both anisotropic. The a-axis (basal plane) conductivity is about 2.5 watts/cm-degree and the c-axis value is about 0.8 watts/cm-degree.[12] Values greater than the above have been reported for highly orientated pyrolytic graphite[9] but are usually less for polycrystalline samples. These samples are also less anisotropic. The c-axis expansion is about 20 times greater than the a-axis for graphite in the 15 to 800°C range.[12] This is a general statement since there is an unexplained contraction in the a-axis up to about 150°C, followed by a range of zero expansion to about 600°C after which the expansion is 0.9×10^{-6}/°C. The value of the c-axis expansion is 28.3×10^{-6}/°C. Less graphitic and polycrystalline samples exhibit less anisotropy and give intermediate values of expansion.[13] The values for carbon blacks range between $4–7 \times 10^{-6}$/°C.[12]

The high thermal stability of graphite is useful in many applications and was the basis for the development of pyrolytic graphite as a refractory material. The melting point of carbon is 3700°C and the boiling point is about 4200°C. It sublimes readily above 3350°C and to lesser extent as low as 2800°C.[4] The mechanical strength of graphite increases with temperature and at higher temperatures exceeds that of tungsten. Pyrolytic graphites have the greatest mechanical strength, particularly at higher temperatures,[9] generally being better than other graphites by a factor of about ten. The relative inertness, especially of pyrolytic graphite, makes graphite a good container material, particularly in metal processing.

Graphite is resistant to the attack of all chemicals except strong oxidizing agents, such as chromic and chlorate solutions.[4] The low porosity of pyrolytic graphite reduces the surface area exposed to a melt, thus reducing possible container contamination. While graphite has many desirable properties, oxidation of the material in air and other oxidizing atmospheres can be exceedingly high and complex depending on a number of variables. This has been reviewed in a fairly recent article.[2]

The purities of carbon, graphite and possibly diamond are far below the values usually considered in electronics, since carbon values are often expressed in percentages. The situation has recently improved with the advent of pyrolytic carbons and new purification techniques. High purity graphite is now available in bulk form with a listed purity of less than ten parts per million. Pyrolytic material is also available in this purity range.

There is a tendency in the literature, and in sections of this chapter, to use the terms carbon and graphite interchangeably. Generally graphite is used where there is three dimensional order in the crystallite and carbon is considered primarily a two dimensional crystal structure with no ordering between the layers. Since it is difficult to determine where orientation between the layering begins to occur, there is a wide range of intermediate structures which are hard to define. Terms such as partially graphitized carbon or turbostratic graphite are often used in this case.

Preparation

Most carbons and graphites used today are manufactured materials which deviate considerably from the ideal structure. Natural graphite is used for some standards and industrial application but is not a major consumption item. The purity of the natural material is usually poor, often containing as much as one per cent impurities. Carbons are prepared in a variety of ways depending on the desired application. Synthetic bulk graphite is prepared mixing a filler of petroleum coke, precalcined to 1300°C, with a coal tar pitch binder.[4] The mixture (called the green mix) is then molded or extruded into the desired shape, followed by heating to 1000°C in the absence of air in order to fuse the filler and binder. The resulting rod, which is 25 to 30 per cent porous, is composed of very small crystallites with more or less randomly oriented layer planes. The porosity can be reduced by impregnation with coal tar pitch, followed by further heating. The crystallites in the carbon are somewhat aligned along the axis of the extruded carbon rods due to the pressure produced during extrusion. The carbon rods are then heat treated to 2500 to 3000°C, converting the disorder layers within the crystallite into a three dimensional structure similar to natural graphite, which is also polycrystalline or mosaic in structure. The resulting rods can then be machined into a variety of shapes.

Carbon black, the second major source of industrial carbon, is formed by the thermal decomposition of volatile hydrocarbons. These may be formed either by impinging partially combusted vapors on a cool surface (channel black) or by thermal cracking in firebrick lined furnaces (furnace black). A wide variety of properties can be produced in these blacks depending on the starting material and the pyrolysis conditions. It should be noted that these blacks are individual unfused particles unlike the bulk material discussed previously. It has been shown[14] that these blacks can also be graphitized at 2800°C similar to bulk graphite provided the average crystallite diameter is above a minimum value. This

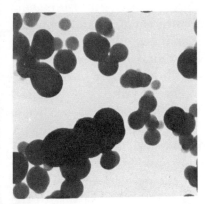 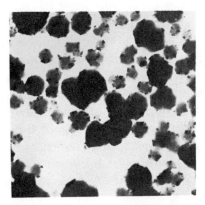

Figure 6-3. Effect of heat treatment on carbon black particles.[14] Left—original carbon black; right—carbon black treated at 2700°C.

results in marked changes in the shape of the individual particles (Figure 6-3) as well as in surface properties.

Pyrolytic graphite, primarily used as a high temperature structural material, is formed by the decomposition of volatile organic materials, usually methane, on a substrate heated to about 1800°C. The pressure of the pyrolyzed gases must be kept low in order to prevent the inclusion of particles, produced by homogeneous decomposition in the gas phase, which degrade the crystallite orientation of the film. When pyrolytic films produced in this manner are heat treated to 3200°C, a graphite structure is produced with an exceedingly high degree of orientation.[15]

The terms hard and soft carbon occur quite frequently in the literature in relationship to graphitizing ability of materials. A soft carbon is a material that can reach a plastic state on heat treatment and hence has a poorly defined graphite structure. Because of the loose structure, the carbon atoms are easily rearranged and, therefore, will graphitize easily. Heat treated coal tar pitch is an example of a soft carbon. Hard carbons, on the other hand, are characterized by a rigid carbon structure which is not easily rearranged and, hence, is difficult to graphitize. Many of the degraded polymer type of organic semiconductors as well as polymers containing oxygen fall into this class.

General Electronic Properties

Many variables must be considered when sensitive measurements such as those for electronic properties are made on any material. The problem of deriving accurate and reproducible results is greatly magnified in the case of carbon since the physical characteristics of this material are often ill-defined. In usual semiconductor measurements, surface effects, physical and chemical defects, and crystallinity are the main concern. In carbon these effects are greatly magnified in relation to the usual semiconductor field, and one must consider, in addition, such factors as the previous history, uniformity of material, and orientation between crystallites. Many measurements are made on compacted powders where pressure is an added factor. This section will deal with the general electronic effects in carbon and its crystalline forms, and an attempt will be made to explain the effects of some of the above characteristics on the electronic properties. Specific cases of semiconduction in carbons will be treated in the next section.

The techniques used for electrical measurements in carbon are essentially the same as those used in the electronics industry. The methods do vary according to the physical condition of the sample. Thus, resistivity measurements may be taken with a four point probe, direct resistivity measurements, or in the case of powders, between leads embedded in the powder prior to compaction. Agreement between these methods is not always satisfactory. Measurements of the energy gap have been reported both from the change of resistivity with temperature and from the absorption edge determined by infrared spectroscopy. The sign of the majority carrier is determined either by thermoelectric power or by Hall measurements. Magnetic properties are also measured for studying electronic properties although the results are often not very clear.

Paramagnetic resonance measurements have been made on carbons which are believed to be related to the unpaired electrons on the crystallite edges. Most graphites are diamagnetic due to the pi electrons along the hexagonal structure. This property is naturally anisotropic. Cyclotron resonance measurements have also been made to determine the effective mass of the conducting electrons. Electron spin data has been collected as a measurement of the unpaired electrons. Spectroscopic data, both infrared and emission, is also available. Many of these techniques are affected by factors other than those being measured (i.e., oxygen affects paramagnetic resonance), and disagreement between authors is common. However, in spite of the disagreements, a rather crude picture of the electronic effects in carbon can be devised.

The diamond form of carbon with a tetrahedral valence is the most perfect crystalline form. This form is similar to the other Group IV semiconductors such as silicon and germanium. Going up the Periodic Table from gray tin, the energy gap increases as does the thermal stability. This continues to diamond which has a high thermal stability and a reported energy gap of 2.8 eV.[16] Among the best conducting diamonds is the Type IIb reported by Custers,[17] which showed p-type semiconductivity with a resistivity of 270 ohm-cm. Hall measurements show between 10^{16} to 10^{17} majority carriers per cc at an energy level about 0.3 eV above the valence band. Crystalline graphite, the other crystalline form, is a conductor along the basal plane or a axis with a resistivity of about 10^4 to 10^5 ohm-cm. The c-axis resistivity is quite low (0.5 to 1 ohm-cm) and apparently has some semiconductor properties. This conduction as well as that of Type IIb diamonds will be discussed in the next section.

Investigations on less crystalline carbons indicate a wide variety of electronic properties primarily related to the heat treatment to which the carbon has been subjected.

The effect of heat treatment or graphitization on electronic properties has been investigated in a general way by Pinnick[6] who used a soft carbon. The most significant change on heat treatment is the resistivity, particularly below 1000°C where the decrease in

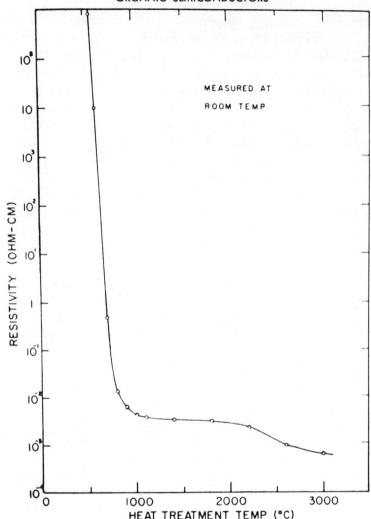

Figure 6-4. Effect of heat treatment on the resisitivity of a soft carbon.[6]

resistivity is about six orders of magnitude (Figure 6-4). At low heat treatment temperatures (up to 500 to 600°C) the material is a disorganized structure containing hydrogen and hydrocarbons bonded to the peripheral carbon atoms of the planes. The bonding is by sigma electrons between the peripheral carbon and the hydrogen or hydrocarbon.

In the heat treatment range between 500 to 800°C, large volumes of hydrogen and hydrocarbon volatilize from the carbon. The peripheral carbon electrons, therefore, are no longer combined with electrons from the absorbed vapors, and these sigma electrons combine with a pi electron from the band to form an electron pair. This, in effect, creates a hole in the filled pi band, as is indicated in the first part of Figure 6-5. Thus, the volatilized vapors cause the creation of a large number of holes which are responsible

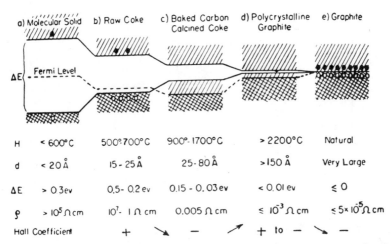

	a) Molecular Solid	b) Raw Coke	c) Baked Carbon Calcined Coke	d) Polycrystalline Graphite	e) Graphite
H	< 600°C	500°-700°C	900°-1700°C	> 2200°C	Natural
d	< 20 Å	15 - 25 Å	25 - 80 Å	> 150 Å	Very Large
ΔE	> 0.3 ev	0.5 - 0.2 ev	0.15 - 0.03 ev	< 0.01 ev	≤ 0
ρ	> 10^5 Ω cm	10^7 - 1 Ω cm	0.005 Ω cm	≤ 10^{-3} Ω cm	≤ 5 × 10^{-5} Ω cm
Hall Coefficient	+	↘	−	↗	+ to − ↘ −

Figure 6-5. Energy band scheme as a function of heat treatment of soft carbon.[a]

for the large drop in resistivity. There is still an energy gap, but the number of holes created is far in excess of thermally excited electrons.

The effect of heat treatment in the 800 to 2000°C range is more complicated, and Hall measurements must be considered before an explanation can be derived. Hall measurement data for a soft carbon is shown in Figure 6-6. It can be seen from the curve that the sign of the majority carrier varies with heat treatment temperature, being positive up to about 1000°C, then negative up to 1700°C, where it again becomes positive up to 2200°C, beyond which it is negative.

Thermoelectric measurements (Figure 6-7) on the same material indicate the same variation. Both of these criteria depend on the reciprocal of the number of carriers so that the maxima and minima occur where the number of carriers is the smallest. If the sign of the Hall coefficient or the thermoelectric power is positive, the predominant carriers are holes; for a negative sign, electronic

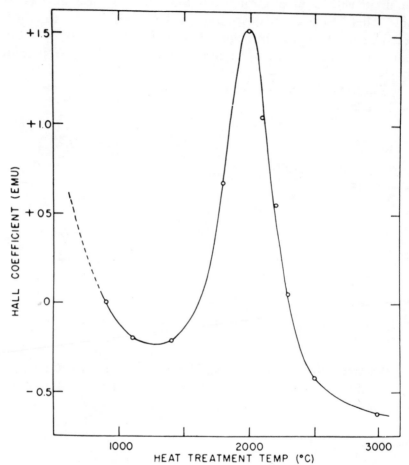

Figure 6-6. Hall coefficient as a function of heat treatment of a soft carbon.[6]

conduction predominates. Thus, in the 800 to 1200°C range, the Hall and thermoelectric measurements indicate a negative slope, or an increasing number of carriers.

However, the resistivity is relatively constant in this region, which could be interpreted as an indication of a negligible change in carrier concentration. According to Pinnick these results can be explained by assuming that so many valence electrons are lost through sigma-pairing in this heat treatment region that eventually a condition is reached in which the electrons remaining in the valence or pi band become the conductors rather than the holes. This is shown schematically in Figure 6-5 where the Fermi level is below the top of the valence band in this heat treatment region. Thus, the minimum produced in the Hall and thermoelectric curves is not due to a greatly increased carrier concentration but

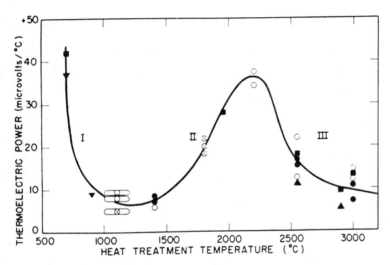

Figure 6-7. Relative theromelectric power as a function of heat treatment of a soft carbon. Measured against platinum.[6]

to a small increase in carriers producing a change in the type of carrier.

In the 1200 to 2000°C heat treatment range most of the peripheral hydrogen and hydrocarbons have been driven off; hence, no more holes are formed. However, the crystallite size gradually increases in this temperature region by a process which is not fully understood. The net result is a decrease in the number of holes, since as the crystallite size increases, the number of edge atoms, on which sigma-pairing occurs, decreases; consequently, electrons are returned to the pi band. In general the increase in crystallite size is not phenomenal, and the decrease in the number of carriers (holes) is offset due to better mobility in the more crystalline material. At temperatures above 2000°C the carbon has attained a fairly high degree of crystallinity. Carbon heated to these temperatures still has an energy gap, but it is in the order of kt at room temperature. The energy gap approaches zero as the heat treatment temperature increases. For larger crystallite samples the energy gap is zero or perhaps negative at 3000°C, where most of the physical properties are identical to those of natural graphite.

Energy gap measurements as a function of heat treatment temperature are also explained in the proposed mechanism (Figure 6-5). The energy gap has been measured using both resistivity vs temperature profiles and the absorption edge determined by infrared spectroscopy. The gradually decreasing energy gap is primarily a function of the increasing crystalline perfection as the heat treatment is increased. At low temperatures the material is essentially a molecular solid, consisting of a carbon structure combined with other organic materials. The Fermi level in this case is in the middle of the forbidden band or energy gap. Between 500 to 700°C, some of the peripheral hydrocarbons or hydrogen are driven off and sigma pairing occurs, causing p-type conduction. The Fermi level is now below the center of the gap. As the heat treatment temperature approaches 1300°C, more surface compounds are lost, causing additional sigma-pairing so that the Fermi level drops into the valence band and finally is so deep in the valence band that the conduction becomes electronic rather than through a hole mechanism. Above 1300°C, most of the surface compounds are driven off, stopping the increase in sigma pairing, and the resulting drop in the Fermi level. Starting around 1700°C, a gradual increase in crystallite size occurs as the heat treatment temperature is increased. This causes a decrease in sigma pairing, discussed previously, which returns electrons to the pi band, in turn raising the Fermi level. This results in p-type conduction which is predominant up to about 2200°C. Electrons, thermally excited to the conduction band, are the predominant carriers in carbons heated above 2200°C. This is made possible by the small energy gap in materials heated above this temperature.

Honda[18] has characterized the graphitization of coal using magnetic susceptibility measurements. From his results he divides heat-treatment effects into five regions as follows:

Semicarbonization	400–700°C
Carbonization	700–1000°C
Semigraphitization	1000–1400°C
Graphitization	1400–2300°C
Crystallization	above 2300°C

He assumes no significant structural changes up to 400°C, but some rearrangements occur above this temperature, causing the formation of paramagnetic components. Above 700°C, the diamagnetic susceptibility increases indicating layer growth. At 1000°C, a constant susceptibility is found where the author assumes decomposition and rearrangement of molecules is still occurring. The 1400 to 2300°C region is the region where the dimensional growth is the primary process, while above this temperature the three-dimensional structure is completed. Honda's description of the graphitization process is not as complete as the one presented by Pinnick,[6] probably because it is based on magnetic susceptibility measurements only. In spite of this, his regions of changing structures and properties are roughly in agreement with Pinnick.

This discussion indicates that carbons might be considered to have room temperature semiconducting properties even when they have been heated to 2000°C. Here one also could point out the similarity of this type of conduction with those of some of the usual organic semiconductors. Thus, the low temperature molecular solids have properties similar to the polyaromatic organic semiconductors. The degraded polymer types of organics have properties similar to carbon heat treated to the raw coke region, although they might also be considered hard carbons since the polymers usually used have a rigid carbon skeleton. A further correlation between complex organic semiconductors and interstitial carbon impurities will be dealt with in a later section.

Semiconducting Carbons

In the previous section semiconduction in carbon was noted in three specific cases, Type IIb diamond, the c axis in graphite, and carbons heat treated at low temperature. A fourth instance, discussed at the end of this section, involves impurities, both interstitial and substitutional. Radiation induced effects will be discussed with impurities, since these effects are similar to those observed for interstitial impurities. The different cases are examined in the order of decreasing crystallinity which does not infer that any one type of carbon is preferable over another in terms of semiconducting properties.

Diamond. Approximate energy gap determinations were made as early as 1934 by Robertson and co-workers.[19] Using optical methods these authors reported an energy gap 2.8 eV. Most diamonds have room temperature resistivity with values as high as 10^{16} ohm-cm being reported.[10] However, a moderate room temperature resistivity has been found in some Type II diamonds which have been labeled Type IIb by Custers[21] in 1952. Since that time several investigations have been made on this type diamond, all of which substantiate the reported semiconductivity.

Austin and Wolfe[22] experimented with a small block 2.99 × 1.53 × 1.52 mm. They used graphite blocks lined with copper, indium, and sharp tungsten wires as contacts. All contacts were non-ohmic, but the results were reproducible. These workers reported a room temperature resistivity of 270 ohm-cm with a positive Hall coefficient. Resistivity measurements were made from −100°C to +600°C (Figure 6-8) and a minimum of 1.5 ohm-cm was found near 500°C. They concluded that the material acted as a normal p-type semiconductor. Using both infrared and resistivity measurements the authors found an acceptor level located 0.38 eV above the valence band. Magnetoresistance measurements, i.e., the change in resistance as a function of the magnetic field strength, were made up to 4000 oersteds with no effect detected.

Magnetoresistance was detected in a different Type IIb diamond by Mitchell and co-workers.[23] The room temperature resistivity of this diamond was 300 ohm-cm and the Hall coefficient was 4.3×10^5 cc/coulomb. The authors detected a transverse (parallel to the width axis) magnetoresistance in field strengths up to 4000 oersteds. A smaller longitudinal magnetoresistance was detected indicating the crystal was anisotropic. Further work on magnetoresistance was performed by Kemmey and Mitchell[24] using three diamonds. From their measurements as well as data reported in the literature, these authors were able to calculate a band structure for IIb diamonds.

Halperin and Nahum[25] measured the energy levels of two Type IIb diamonds using both conductivity and optical measurements. Thermoluminescence, photoconductivity, and dark conductivity were also investigated by these workers. Whereas most authors report one energy level (acceptor level) in the energy gap, five discrete levels were reported by these authors at 0.21, 0.30, 0.37, 0.52, and 0.7 eV above the valence band. An additional level was

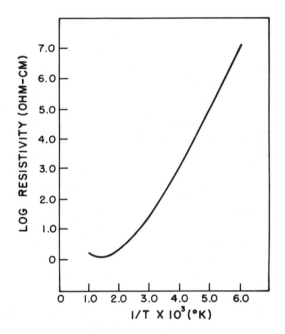

Figure 6-8. Resistivity of type IIb diamond as a function of temperature.[23]

detected near the middle of the gap by thermoluminescent measurements which was considered to be due to a recombination center. The properties of several diamonds (4 insulator and 2 Type IIb) have been investigated in the microwave region.[26] The room temperature resistivity of the Type IIb specimens was 130 ohm-cm and the energy gap was 2.8 eV.

These values were determined by a different method than used by other workers and the results are at least in qualitative agreement. This may be significant since, while only a small number of Type IIb diamonds have been investigated, all results seem to be in agreement. No electrical measurements have been found in the literature on synthetically produced semiconducting diamonds, but work is being done in this field.

The theory of semiconduction in Type IIb diamonds derived from the experimental information, is fairly well developed. The actual cause of semiconduction, however, has not been definitely established. While the semiconduction is assumed to be due to physical defects or impurities, no actual experiments have been performed to determine which of the foregoing are responsible for the discrete energy levels within the energy gap. The concentration of the defects, whether physical or chemical, is assumed to be responsible for the variation in resistivity between the samples investigated.

Graphite. All of the diamond measurements were made on natural materials from the same source and consequently have a similar past history. Graphite, however, is not only a natural material, but is produced synthetically in several forms. Because of the large variation in physical properties of the available graphite, knowledge of the source of the material is an important factor when considering the resulting electrical properties. Three principal sources will be considered in this section: natural graphite, polycrystalline graphite, and pyrolytic graphite.

The electrical conductivity of natural graphite was measured by Primak and Fuchs[27] in 1954. These workers measured the conductivity in the a and c directions of graphite crystals which had been purified by extended leaching in hydrochloric and hydrofluoric acid followed by heat treatment to 3000°C. This purification reduced the total impurity level from 0.5 per cent to 150 ppm (parts per million), the remaining impurities being aluminum, arsenic, calcium, potassium, phosphorous, strontium, and zinc.

Visual observation was used to determine crystallinity. The electrical measurements were made on ten graphite crystals. The ratio of the c- to a-axis resistivities was about 400, but there was a 50 per cent variation in the ratio for the ten crystals examined. The a-axis resistivity averaged 2.6×10^{-4} ohm-cm with good agreement between crystals. The average c-axis resistivity was about 0.02 ohm-cm with more variation than in the a-axis results. Increasing the temperature increased the c-axis resistivity more significantly than the a-axis resistivity.

Dutta[28] performed similar experiments on natural graphite and found a ratio of the c- to a-axis resistivity of about 10^4. Primak attributed the difference in results between Dutta's work and his own work to sample preparation. Dutta found the resistivity along the a-axis increased with temperature while the c-axis resistivity decreased with temperature. This effect was not reported by Primak and Fuchs, who worked mostly below room temperature. There is some indication in their work of a decreasing resistivity in the c axis above 250°K, however. Dutta's value of the c-axis resistivity is about two orders of magnitude higher than that of Primak and Fuchs.

Primak[29] continued his investigation using a more perfect crystal which had been examined by X-ray diffraction. The crystal was more carefully treated than in the previous work on the assumption that even very light pressure could produce distortion of the crystal. The sample was quite small, being 0.01 cm thick and 0.15 cm long. The results agreed with his previous work. It was concluded that nonuniform current flow was the principal reason for the resistivity variations along the c axis.

Grisdale[3] also worked with natural graphite crystals in 1951. He reported a c-axis resistivity of 0.01 ohm-cm, an a-axis resistivity of 3.9×10^{-5} ohm-cm, and an energy gap (c axis) of 0.025 eV. Blackman, et al.,[30] also working with natural graphite crystals (examined by X-ray diffraction) found an a-axis resistivity of 2×20^{-3} ohm-cm in samples containing 2 per cent impurities. This is similar to the values reported by Primak and Fuchs for a much higher purity, which indicates that impurities are not too significant in a-axis measurements. Blackman reported c-axis resistivities of 0.25 and 0.5 ohm-cm, in agreement with Dutta's values, as well as a negative temperature coefficient of resistance.

This brief survey does not include all values reported in the literature. However, most authors agree quite well on the a-axis resistivity. The question of the c-axis resistivity may be more fully answered in the discussion of pyrolytic graphite.

Hall effect measurements are difficult with natural graphite because of the problems of sample preparation. Breckinridge[31] used a near perfect crystal with a reported purity of 2 ppm which had been purified by chlorination at 3000°C. He found the sign of the Hall coefficient was negative at large field strengths and positive at low field strengths which indicated several different charge carriers were present. McClure[32] in a theoretical paper explained this effect as the result of the electrons and hole carriers being of approximately the same concentration. Soule[33] also measured Hall effect and magnetoresistance of graphite crystals at several temperatures. From his experimental results he calculated the effective mass of the electrons was 0.030 M_0 while the effective mass of the holes was 0.060 M_0. He also calculated that there is a 0.030 eV overlap of the energy bands in the a direction of crystalline graphite.

More work has been done on the electrical and magnetic properties of synthetic polycrystalline graphite because of the greater availability of this material. While measurements on single crystals have been confined to resistivity and a few other simple experiments, a much larger variety of measurements have been made on synthetic material. However, in artificial graphite, polycrystallinity and structural disorders are present to a larger extent which means more caution is necessary in the interpretation of results, especially in the case of magnetic measurements.

Resistivity measurements on the a-axis are about 10^{-3} to 10^{-4} ohm-cm at room temperature[6] similar to natural crystals, even in cases where the crystallite alignment is not perfect. The ratio of resistivity between the a and c axes is much less, however, as a result of misalignment. Mal'tsova[34] found the resistivity across an extruded rod to be only twenty per cent greater than along the extrusion axis. A ratio of 1.3 has also been reported.[4] The effect of porosity on resistivity measurements on extruded rods was also investigated by Mal'tsova.[34] He reported the following resistivities at 1000°C as a function of density:

Density (g/cc)	Resistivity (1000°C)
1.73	6.4
1.67	9.2
1.46	12.9
1.43	7.6

An additional problem in resistivity measurements has been by Bhattacharyya[35] who found that chemical pretreatment of graphite lowered the a-axis resistivity and increased the c-axis resistivity. This effect could explain some of the disagreement on the resistivity of natural graphite reported earlier in this section.

Hall measurements on polycrystalline samples are quite common, but the results are often not too clear. Pinnick[6] found n-type conduction in polycrystalline rods, but Mrozowski[36] found p-type conduction using compressed graphitized carbon blacks which had been heat treated to 2800°C. The carbon black used in this case (P-33) has a large particle diameter and should graphitize satisfactorily at 2800°C. The data of Schaeffer, Smith, and Polley[14] indicate a d spacing of 3.41 A and an average crystallite diameter of 200 A for this material heated to 2800°C. The Hall coefficient is probably not too significant in this case, however, since compressed powders of graphitized carbon blacks would not be expected to show preferential orientation even under pressure. Magnetoresistance measurements on polycrystalline graphite have been performed by Mrozowski and Chabershi[37] who find a positive effect both at liquid nitrogen and room temperature. Since these measurements were made at only one field strength, the variation in sign of the majority carrier reported by Breckinridge[31] would not be detected.

Magnetic susceptibility has been measured by several authors who report that graphite is diamagnetic due to the oriented hexagonal structure of graphite. The reported values are a function of the average crystalline size.[6] As expected, the diamagnetic effect is anisotropic being forty-four times greater in the c axis than in the a axis[38] which has a reported value of -5×10^{-6} cgs units/g. Small paramagnetic effects have been reported by Hennig both in natural and artificial graphite.[39] In his work, he found a relatively high concentration of spin centers (10^{-3} per atom) which he attributed to the mosaic structure of the materials. The samples were ground, acid treated, and heat treated to 3000°C, which might have introduced a large number of spin centers due to breakage and distortion of the crystallites even in natural graphite. His data checked fairly well with the number of edge atoms assumed from crystallite size measurements based on X-ray line widths (2×10^{-3} edge atom). This is at best an approximation, however, for the large crystallite sizes (> 1000 A) present in natural crystals.

Electron spin resonance has been applied to graphite by Mrozowski[40] to determine the number of spin centers produced on the peripheral carbon atoms as the crystallite size was decreased by grinding, which again may have produced other distortions beside decreasing the crystallite size. Mrozowski estimated that about one-fourth of the edge atoms behaved as spin centers. Exposure to air caused the resonance to disappear; thus, it is possible that this estimate may be low since residual gases in the graphite may have nullified some of the spin centers.

Thermoelectric power measurements on polycrystalline graphite have been reported by several authors. Pinnick[6] reported a negative value for soft carbon heated to 3000°C. Mrozowski[36] measured the effect of pressure (up to 6000 psi) on the thermoelectric power of graphitized carbon blacks and found no change. His values, measured against platinum are much higher than reported by Pinnick on the soft carbon (~ 50 μV/°C compared to ~ 8μV/°C). Ubbelohde and Orr[11] measured the thermoelectric power in both the a and c directions using a variety of materials. They reported a value of -9 μV/°C in the a axis and $+6\mu$V/°C in the c axis and suggest the possibility of a graphite-graphite thermocouple. Such a thermocouple has since been constructed by these authors.[42]

The results using polycrystalline graphite indicate that there is often poor agreement between authors due to variations in the material used. At this point a material will be discussed which generally has more reproducible properties. Pyrolytic graphite is not a new material, having been patented as early as 1880.[4] However, with the need for new structure materials, this type of carbon has undergone considerable investigation in the past few years. Most of the work has been done on structural properties, but some work on electronic properties has been reported.

Pyrolytic graphite is formed by the thermal decomposition of carbon containing vapors on a hot substrate as discussed earlier in this chapter. Recent studies[43] have shown that the chemical nature of the substrate has no effect on the deposit, but that surface roughness of the substrate does influence the growth rate and crystalline perfection. There is also some evidence of surface mobility during the deposition. When heated to sufficiently high temperatures, a structure closely resembling crystalline graphite is produced. At temperatures above 2500°C, a d spacing of 3.35 A and an average crystallite size of 500 A has been reported.[44] The orientation between crystallites is high with values above 99.9 per cent orientation having been obtained.[45]

The electrical measurements also indicate a high degree of orientation. There is some evidence that pyrolytic graphite tends to be turbostatic (disordered in the c direction) rather than having the usual ABAB configuration, although samples heated to 2800°C for two hours seem to give good three-dimensional X-ray patterns.[46] The room temperature resistivity (a-axis) of well ordered pyrolytic graphite is about 10^{-4} ohm-cm which is somewhat higher than the lowest resistivity reported for natural graphite crystals but lower than values reported for artificial graphite.[45] The c-axis resistivity is 0.5 ohm-cm which is close to the value reported by Dutta (1 ohm-cm) and other workers. Klein[45] reported that the c-axis resistivity increased with increasing heat treatment. His ratio of the conductivity of the a to c axis is about 10^4 in agreement with Dutta's value of this ratio. Similar results were reported by Brown and Watt using a material that had been pyrolyzed to 2100°C.[47] Hall measurements[45] were found to be virtually independent of both the current and magnetic field intensity. However, both positive and negative Hall coefficients were found with no relation to the deposition temperature. There was a correlation between the coefficient sign and the Franklin index (Figure 6-2). Samples with low d spacings, indicating good three-dimensional orientation, were n-type while poorly orientated samples (larger d spacings) were p-type. Magnetoresistance measurements at room temperature indicated a decrease of resistivity of about 50 per cent at a field strength of 25 kilogauss which is intermediate between natural and artificial graphite.[48]

Klein indicated that the Hall coefficients reflected only the perfection of layer orientation while the magnetoresistance reflected the crystallite alignment and increased rapidly with the degree of preferred orientation. He concluded that the carrier concentration was in the order of 6×10^{18}/cc with the concentration of electron and hole carriers being equal. This is in agreement with the values reported by Soule[33] for natural graphite. The carrier mobility (a direction) is about 2×10^3 cm^2/V sec at room temperature, about an order of magnitude less than reported in natural graphite.[45] Klein reported a somewhat higher carrier concentration in a later paper[49] and a mobility ratio, electrons to holes, of 1.08. Diamagnetic susceptibilities were measured on pyrolytic graphites by Fishback[51] who found a correlation between this effect and the heat treatment temperature. Samples heated to 3000 to 3400°C resulted in a diamagnetism between the values reported for natural and artificial graphite crystals.

The preceding review indicates some disagreement on the measured electrical and magnetic properties of graphite. In general, it might be concluded that the best values are those for natural crystals, the pyrolytic graphite values are intermediate, and the artificial graphite values are the least reliable. Using this criteria, the most reliable values of various parameters are given in Table 6-1.

Table 6-1. Electronic Parameters of Graphite.

Parameter	a direction	c direction
Resistivity, ohm-cm	10^{-5}	1
Charge carriers	p and n	p
Mobility, cm^2/volt-sec	2×10^4	—
Mobility ratio, e/h	1.08	—
Carrier density—holes	3×10^{18}	—
—electrons	3×10^{18}	—
Effective mass—holes	$.060\ M_0$	—
—electrons	$.030\ M_0$	—

Using structural considerations as well as experimental results, the band structure of graphite has been investigated by several workers. All models refer to conduction only in the a direction where the pi band is split into a filled valence band and an empty conduction band. These bands are either just touching or slightly overlapping. The calculations involved are discussed in the work of Corbato,[52], McClure,[32] and Heering and Wallace.[53] The subject will not be further discussed in this chapter since the c-axis rather than the a-axis conductivity is of interest in terms of semiconducting properties.

Low Temperature Carbons. The carbons discussed in the foregoing paragraphs were crystalline or near crystalline forms in which semiconduction was noted in one crystalline direction and metallic conduction in another crystalline direction. In this section a much more disordered form is discussed which also has some semiconducting properties. It is in this form that carbon technology resembles that of degradated polymers. The possibility of semiconduction in this range (below 1000°C) was discussed earlier where with low temperature heat treatment, a measurable energy gap and fairly good resistivity were observed. The resistivity and energy gap increase rapidly with decreasing temperature and essentially become insulators below 600°C. The large change in properties as a function of heat treatment in this range would indicate that reproducibility between experiments would require extremely closely controlled conditions. If this could be achieved, however, carbon with a great variety of electrical properties could be produced. Most investigators do not consider the 600 to 1000°C range as a separate subject but only as part of heat treatment studies extending to about 3000°C as discussed previously. As a result information on the electrical properties in this range is somewhat limited.

Schaeffer, Smith, and Polley[14] in a paper on the heat treatment of carbon blacks measured electrical properties as well as several other parameters in this range. They found a less marked decrease than Pinnick[6] which would be expected with a carbon that had been heated previously during the formation of the black. Little change in crystallite size was detected ($L_a \sim 30$ A) and no three-dimensional orientation was observed. Carbon dioxide and carbon monoxide were evolved during heat treatment, mostly before 600°C, but some was still driven off at higher temperatures (Figure 6-9). Hydrogen evolution began at 600°C and reached a maximum at 1000°C. The gases evolved were probably from crystallite edges and could have effected the resistivity by the sigma pairing mechanism previously discussed.

Uebersfield[53] measured the paramagnetic resonance of coals and chars heated to 900°C. He related the number of spin centers in the carbon to hydrogen ratio in his materials and found the maximum ($\sim 7 \times 10^{19}$/cc) to occur with a carbon to hydrogen ratio of

33. In agreement with work noted earlier in this chapter, he found that oxygen decreased the concentration of the spin centers. Further electronic considerations were not made in this work since the author was primarily seeking a criteria to estimate the graphitizability of various coals. Electron spin resonance measurements have been made on numerous materials[40] which indicate that the number of spin centers is quite high and related to the number of carriers in the carbon (p-type in this case). The general theory,

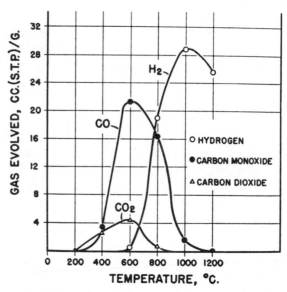

Figure 6-9. The evolution of gases during low temperature heat treatment.[14]

again, is that as the gases are desorbed, electrons are removed from the pi band by sigma bonding at the spin centers, increasing the hole concentration which is estimated to be higher than 2×10^{20} carriers/cc in this paper.

Electron spin resonance also was the subject of several papers at the Fifth Carbon Conference[54] at which it was concluded that the resonance was due to charge carriers in heat treated graphite, but no conclusions were drawn in relation to the low temperature carbons. While results for electron spin resonance are not conclusive, Mrozowski[55] has indicated the following points:

(1) A strong intensity maximum occurs when samples are heated at 700°C indicating a concentration of 2×10^{20} spin centers/cc. The intensity drops off 50 per cent at 100° above or below 700°C.

(2) Paramagnetic gases (mainly oxygen) reduce the line intensity.

(3) Intensity is a function of spin centers produced by broken sigma bonds on carbon atoms.

Resistivity measurements have been made by other authors and in general the results are similar to those produced in degredated polymers.[56] A p-type conductivity was also found in the 600 to 800°C range by Weiss[57] who ascribed the result to electronic interaction between carbonyl and ether groups through the aromatic residue, presumably the carbon. In view of the work of Schaeffer, Smith, and Polley,[14] indicating most of the oxygen is driven off below 800°C as carbon oxides, this assumption does not seem valid.

The work thus far discussed has been on bulk or powdered samples. In cases like this porosity, random orientation and the pressure of compaction (for powders) can cause variable results. Pyrolytic films have been prepared by some workers to eliminate these factors. Grisdale[3] used this technique for the production of pyrolytic film resistors. Using boron as an additive, he recorded resistivities between one and 10^{-3} ohm-cm. Knispel[58] produced films by the pyrolysis of ethyl chloride at 450°C, and found the resistivity varied with the film thickness but was greater than for graphite. The resistivity increased with increasing gas pressure during formation and decreased with increasing deposition temperature. Dutta and Chowdhury[59] reported the basal plane conductivity increased with film thickness. Their measurements were on a more graphitic material than is being considered here, however. They attributed the thickness effect to nonuniform current flow. Toyoda and Nagashima[60] reported the resistivity of their films was inversely proportional to thickness up to 500 A, after which the current was constant with thickness. They used evaporated carbon films which tend to be quite graphitic. A negative temperature coefficient was also detected in their work.

There has been considerable effort to produce carbon films at 1000°C or higher,[61] but information on the production of films below this temperature is quite limited. The author is presently

engaged in a study to attempt to correlate the electronic properties
with other physical properties of low temperature carbons. In this
work[62] anthracene, naphthalene, and phenanthrene are decomposed
on quartz to form removable films. Resistivity and energy gap
measurements are made on the films as well as chemical analysis
and diffraction studies. The starting material is found to be less
important than the formation temperature (Figure 6-10). The

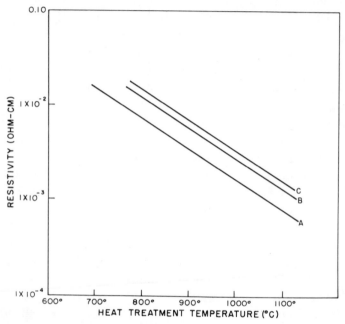

Figure 6-10. Resistivity as a function of formation temperature
for carbon films.[62] A. Naphthalene, B. Anthracene, C. Phenanthrene.

data shown in this figure should be regarded as approximate since
there is considerable deviation from the curves for some of the
points. In addition, it would be expected that the slope would not
be constant, particularly at lower temperatures. In agreement with
other workers the crystallite size does not change significantly in
this heat treatment range, nor is there any three-dimensional
orientation, although the resistivity changes several orders of
magnitude. Micrographs (Figure 6-11) indicate an entirely different microstructure depending on the starting material, but the

electrical properties decomposed at the same temperature are still similar. The energy gap decreases with increasing temperature being about 0.15 eV for 700°C materials and 0.02 eV at 1000°C. Thus, these results also seem to agree with those of other workers.

The actual cause of semiconduction in these carbons has never

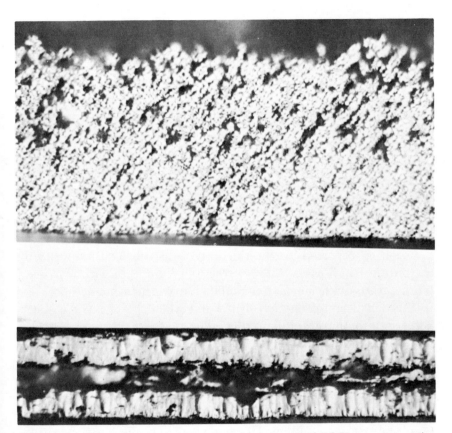

Figure 6-11. Micrographs of carbon films formed at 800°C.[62] Top—cross section of pyrolyzed phenathrene (×700); bottom—cross section of pyrolyzed naphthalene (×700).

been definitely established, but it is generally agreed that these properties are the result of edge effects between the crystallites. The crystallite size is less important than the condition of the crystallite edges. The present theory assumes that atoms other than carbon (such as oxygen and hydrogen) at the crystallite edges produce a small insulating effect at the edges which gives semi-conducting properties to the bulk material. This could be explained in terms of a mechanism in which the edge electrons are combined with electrons from the foreign atoms causing a band of non-conducting electrons through which conduction electrons must migrate. However, more work must be done on these materials before a true mechanism can be determined.

Impurity and Radiation Induced Effects in Graphite

Impurity effects have been the subject of many investigations in recent years, since tremendous changes are found in crystalline graphite as a result of chemical treatment. Radiation damage effects have also been studied, but the effects are much less pronounced than impurity effects. The subject has been reviewed in a recent book by Ubbelohde and Lewis.[63] Hennig[64] had divided these effects into five classifications: lattice vacancies, ordered and disordered interstitial compounds, substitutional impurities, and radiation induced disorders. These effects will be reviewed in the following paragraphs.

Boron is reported to be the only substitutional impurity in graphite.[64] In all cases, a lower resistivity graphite with a positive temperature coefficient is found. The boron acts as an acceptor due to the deficiency of one covalent bond when the element is incorporated into the graphite lattice. The decrease in resistivity was quite small ($R/R_0 \sim 0.9$ for 10^5 atoms/cc) and considerably less than predicted by Hennig (Figure 6-12) who attributed this to a lower mobility due to increased scattering and to incomplete ionization of the boron. Soule[65] also investigated boron doped graphite over a wide range of doping extending from two per cent to less than one part per million. He concluded that the boron was completely ionized at dilute concentrations where near ideal conditions exist. The electron scattering due to the boron was also found to be low. Soule also reported Hall measurements which indicated the formation of excess holes by the boron addition.

Boron was also incorporated into the lattice by Albert and Parisot[66] who used boric acid mixed with coke or carbon black. Portions of the mix were graphitized at 1800°C and at 2500°C using induction heating. The samples were compressed prior to graphitization and measurements were made parallel and perpendicular to the compression direction. The assumption in this case is that compression would tend to align the crystallites to some extent causing the basal planes to be perpendicular to the compression direction. Experiments were performed using undoped carbons and carbons doped with 0.8 per cent boron. The boron increased the conductance both parallel and perpendicular to the

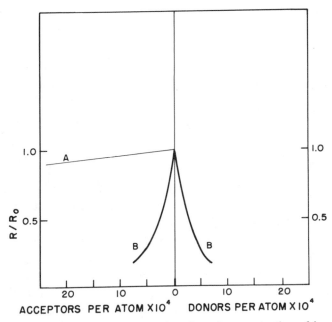

Figure 6-12. Resistance as a function of concentration of impurities in graphite.[61] A. Boron, experimental results; B. theoretical curve.

compression direction in the material heated to 2500°C. A slight increase in resistivity was found in boron doped samples heated to 1100 and 1800°C. Boron carbide (B_4C) was also added to the carbons producing similar results. In all of the results on boron doped graphite and carbon there is a question as to whether the boron is homogeneous in the matrix or is present as clusters. This is particularly true of the last work discussed.[66]

Ubbelohde[67] has postulated that, in addition to boron, group V and VI atoms could be added to the graphite lattice to obtain donor sites which might be expected to increase the resistivity.

The larger size of the impurity atom in this case would tend to distort the lattice and give anomalous scattering, if these materials could be incorporated. There has been only limited work on the incorporation of these materials into the graphite lattice, to the author's knowledge, although the addition of impurity atoms to inorganic semiconductors such as germanium and silicone have been extensively studied. They are considerably different materials from graphite however.

The interstitial compounds were the primary subject of the recent review by Ubbelohde.[63] A large number of compounds, both metallic and nonmetallic, have been prepared. The impurity atoms are incorporated between the larger planes in a more or less ordered structure and in many cases can be removed after addition without effecting the lattice structure. Stoichiometric compounds are reported in literature, but many additions are not stoichiometric. Molecular additions as opposed to atomic additions are also possible. Croft[69] reported a large number of these although his experimental data is somewhat limited. The compounds are usually made by direct combination of the constituents, although sometimes heat is necessary.

The electrical properties of interstitial graphite compounds have been reviewed both by Ubbelohde[70] and Blackman.[12] The electrical conductivity of graphite with interstitial impurities exceeds that of pure graphite regardless of the nature of the impurity. Hennig[71] reported that bisulfate addition increased the conductivity and Ubbelohde[72] reported the same for bromine-graphite and potassium-graphite. McDonnell, Pick, and Ubbelohde[73] give a qualitative explanation for these results by postulating that electropositive interstitial impurities donate electrons to the empty pi band while electronegative interstitial impurities draw electrons from the filled pi band (valence band), creating holes. Thus, there is an increase in carriers regardless of the type of impurity (Figure 6-12). In general a limiting value of $R/R_0 = 0.1$ is found in the a-axis resistivity.

Resistivity measurements in the c-direction have not been reported until recently because of the physical instability of interstitial graphite compounds produced from polycrystalline graphite. Results using well orientated pyrolytic graphite, however, indicate a 200-fold increase in c-direction conductivity, for a potassium-graphite compound.[12] There is a more pronounced increase for alkali metal (donor) additions than for halogen (acceptor) additions. Ubbelohde postulates the graphite layers become strongly polarized by the interstitial atoms, the alkali metals having more effect than the halogens, thus facilitating conduction along the c axis. Diamagnetic susceptibility measurements show a marked decrease in susceptibility as interstitial impurities are added which is attributed to changes in the band structure as a result of electron transfer between the impurities and the lattice carbon atoms. Hennig[74] reported that progressive bromination of graphite resulted in an increasing Hall coefficient which changed from negative to positive at a bromine concentration of about 1.5×10^{20} atoms/g. This is in agreement with McDonnell, Pick and Ubbelohde[73] who predicted that halogens would draw electrons from the valence band to produce holes as stated previously.

Marked changes in thermoelectric power have been reported for interstitial compounds in both the a and c directions.[75] The addition of potassium (C_{1000} K) changed the thermoelectric power in the a direction from —5 to —10 $\mu V/°C$ while bromine addition (C_{220} Br) changed this value from —5 to +37 $\mu V/°C$. In the c-direction potassium (C_{1000} K) caused a change from +6 to —11 $\mu V/°C$ while bromine (C_{220} Br) caused the thermoelectric power to increase from +6 to +54 $\mu V/°C$. These authors also discussed the effects of physical defects on the thermoelectric power. Hennig[76] attempted, without success, to determine superconductivity in these materials by cooling interstitial compounds of bromine, potassium, calcium, boron, ammonium ion, and bisulfate ion graphites down to 1.25°K. Photoelectric effects have also been reported in cesium-graphite interstitial compounds.[17]

Radiation induced effects have not been investigated as completely as impurity effects, but some data are available on the subject. Myers and Larson[78] measured the resistivity of reactor grade graphite irradiated with 2 Mev electrons and noted three effects. First, there was a transient change of resistivity during irradiation caused by electron-hole pairs produced by the radiation. A second effect was caused by the heating of the sample during irradiation resulting in a resistivity change due to the temperature dependence of this property. The third effect, and the only permanent one, was the result of lattice damage. Radiation damage studies have also been performed by Hennig[67] who found that electrons, protons, deuterons, and neutrons always produce excess acceptor states as revealed by Hall measurements. The acceptors are believed to be interstitial atoms, but lattice vacancies may also be acceptor sites. Hennig believes that, with the exception of electron irradiated graphite, the occurrence of these effects is not homogeneous, but the effects occur in clusters. The creation of new acceptor levels caused a marked resistivity increase in irradiated graphite (as measured in the a direction) some of which was probably due to increased scattering as a result of lattice damage.

Pyrolytic carbons have also been the subject of radiation damage studies.[79] In this work a two order of magnitude increase in resistivity was found for near ideal graphite after irradiation with a less marked change detected for more poorly orientated carbons. These were resistivity measurements along the a axis. Measurements were also made along the c-axis where a resistivity decrease from 0.5 to 0.07 ohm-cm was reported. It is suspected in this case that the interstitial carbons produced by irradiation act as a bridge between the layer carbons. A positive Hall effect, in agreement with Hennig, is also reported in this work.

Montet[80] reported on the retention of protons induced into graphite by a glow discharge and found the activation for movement of hydrogen through graphite to be 13 kcal. Since he could detect no change in electrical properties, however, it is assumed that the electrical changes produced by irradiation are effects due to lattice changes rather than radiation by-products. Lattice vacancies of the type caused by irradiation can also be caused by cooling of the graphite. The true effect of these defects is difficult to determine, since both cooling and irradiation can produce other types of defects which can mask the lattice vacancy influence. This has been discussed by Grenall.[81] Several types of lattice vacancies are depicted by Ubbelohde[82] in his recent book and will not be elaborated upon in this discussion.

Possible Utilization of Graphite

The preceding section is not intended to be a complete survey, but only a review of some of the better known work on carbon and its crystalline form. This brief review, however, does serve to indicate that while a great deal of effort has been expended on the electronic properties of carbon, the results are often inconsistent. Thus, the general properties are known on a qualitative basis, but quantitative results vary usually due to sample variations. Perhaps a standard material is needed by the industry in order that experiments can be duplicated by other workers in the field. The most desirable material for a standard would probably be a high temperature pyrolytic graphite, since the purity of this material is better than most graphites. This material is fairly easy to prepare and should be both abundant and inexpensive. It has the disadvantage of being well oriented but microcrystalline or mosaic in structure. In addition, the degree of orientation between the hexagonal layers is not definitely known. In spite of these factors, however, the reproducibility in experiments using pyrolytic graphite seems to be better than for natural or other synthetic graphites.

Another general problem of all carbons discussed in this chapter is the presence of several types of physical defects that are inherent in all forms of the material. While massive defects such as pores are present only in some carbons and graphites, smaller defects such as dislocations are present in all cases. Recent results on these dislocations have been reported by several workers using electron microscopy. These studies generally involve transmission of the beam through thin sections of graphite since this material is highly transparent to electrons.[81] Grenall and Sosin,[81] using this technique, found both simple and complex distortions in natural graphite subjected to thermal stresses due to the electron beam. Slip and climb distortions were detected along the basal plane which moved slowly under thermal stress. Numerous complex networks were also photographed which slowly changed form, eventually broke up, and disappeared. Some pinned dislocations were also observed. The authors discussed five possible dislocations (three edge, one mixed, and one screw) and gave examples from their experimental work. Tsuzuku[83] investigated the dislocations formed by the stress produced during graphitization of a soft carbon. He calculated that a pressure of about 10^{10} dynes/cm^2 is imparted to material heated to 2600°C due to the interference of anisotropically expanding crystallites. This leads to buckling in the crystallites which causes the spontaneous formation of dislocations. The dislocations then migrate in such a way as to relieve the remaining stress in the material. It appears that the author assumed no dislocations remained in the crystallites but all migrated to the boundaries.

Williamson[84] investigated dislocation loops in graphite formed by the condensation of vacancies and interstitial atoms. He postulated that only the interstitial atoms are mobile below 1200°C, while above this temperature the vacancies also migrate into clusters. The loops formed at lower temperatures were annealed out of the crystallites at 1500°C. Williamson also indicated that tilted twin boundaries are formed as a result of distortion. Bacon and Sprague[85] found precipitation of impurities occurring at grain boundaries and also that impurities slowed the dislocation motion but did not pin dislocations. Neutron irradiation damage, however, did effectively pin the dislocations. In summary then, the following dislocations have been investigated in graphite:

        (a) interstitial atoms
        (b) vacancies
        (c) stacking defects
        (d) twinned planes
        (e) edge defects
        (f) thermally induced distortions
        (g) dislocation loops

An additional factor, often considered a type of defect, is the impurity content of graphite and carbon.

Impurities can produce extreme effects on the properties of carbons as has been demonstrated by Gulbransen and Andrew[86] who found a small increase in the iron concentration in graphite increased the oxidation rate by a factor over 500. However, in reviewing the literature, references to the purity of the materials used are extremely rare. In most cases where the carbon has been purified by the investigators, no reference has been made to the degree of purity which has been obtained by the various treatments applied. This factor serves to emphasize the point that many workers have failed to properly characterize the carbon with which they have been working. In view of the complexity of the material, extremely divergent results can be found which might be explained if more was known about the specific sample used.

This is probably the principal reason that a clear quantitative picture of the physical and chemical properties has not been obtained. This again indicates the desirability of an industrial standard for graphite since very few laboratories have the equipment necessary to perform all the measurements required for an accurate determination of the properties of the material.

It is difficult to see any electronic application of carbon, aside from electrodes, ever accounting for a significant portion of the total production of the material. It is probably for this reason that studies of the electronic properties of the material tend to be concentrated in organizations which are more aligned with basic research. The interest has generally been academic in that the investigations have been undertaken without a definite product in mind. Some of the data, however, might be used as a basis for product development. It is the purpose of this section to elucidate on some of the available information which might indicate application possibilities.

A number of possibilities exist for carbon in the semiconductor field, although these applications are quite remote. The use of Type IIb diamond as a high temperature material is being investigated, although no actual devices are available. The problem of making a p-n junction in diamond has not as yet been solved and could be a serious limitation to this application. It is assumed that junctions would have to be made by diffusion of an n-type dopant into the lattice. Epitaxially grown junctions on diamond surfaces would be difficult since a high pressure would probably be needed to prevent graphite formation. The production of junctions during the pressure synthesis of diamonds would be extremely difficult at the present state of the art.

The lack of knowledge of the exact conduction mechanism in diamond is another factor which would limit its application at the present time. Silver can be used as an effective contact and lead material for this application.[24] Diamond is the only crystal form of carbon where the tetrahedral valence exists and, hence, could be applied using existing semiconductor theory.

Other carbon forms are similar in structure to organic semiconductors where the theory of semiconduction is quite nebulous. The usefulness of the c-axis semiconductivity in graphite would be highly limited due to the low resistivity in this direction and the over-all lack of knowledge of the electronic properties in the c direction. The conductivity is generally p-type in this direction but little is known on the effects of doping on the properties in this direction. It is probable that any n-type dopant would form an interstitial compound rather than combine in the lattice, because of atomic size considerations. Since all interstitial compounds tend to decrease the resistivity, any attempt to dope graphite in order to produce a junction in the c axis would not be expected to be successful.

Employment of low temperature pyrolyzed carbons seems somewhat more favorable because of the possibility of varying the properties by heat treatment. Thus, a base material can be produced with almost any desired resistivity. These materials are usually p-type and would be expected to have a large number of majority and minority carriers, but probably a low mobility due to the defect structure. It is likely that junctions could be produced in this material by doping which would in effect change the character of the crystallite edges where the semiconductivity is believed to occur. The reproducibility of these materials is not reliable at the present time.

It is the belief of the author that films present the best approach, since this eliminates at least some of the variables involved. The resulting devices would probably not be extremely tolerant nor useful at high temperatures because of the small energy gap. Care would have to be exercised in attaching leads because of the tendency of a large number of materials to diffuse into the carbon. This type of carbon approximates the properties (and problems) of many of the degraded polymer type of organic semiconductor and hence the difficulties enumerated here also exist for this type of material when semiconduction is being considered.

Electronic applications other than in the semiconductor device field have been indicated in the literature. Photoconductivity has been measured in Type IIb diamond by Halperin and Nahum[25] who found it to be completely masked by the dark conductivity at room temperature but were able to detect a photoconductivity at liquid air temperatures with a wavelength of 2200 A. Any application of this would be of dubious value, however. Setton and Bazin[77] found a photoconductive effect in a cesium-graphite interstitial compound, but little is known on the magnitude of the effect nor the particulars of the experiment.

The thermoelectric power measurements reported by various authors vary, but these measurements do indicate that graphite may have some application at least as a thermocouple material. In fact two types of graphite thermocouples have been reported in the literature. The first mentioned previously in this chapter was reported by Ubbelohde[76] who used graphite oriented with the a axis (n-type) coupled with polycrystalline graphite. The thermocouple was calibrated up to 2400°C and had a thermoelectric power of about 18 μV/°C. The second thermocouple was reported by Shepard[87] who used a graphite (n-type) to boron doped graphite (p-type) couple which has been successful in at least one application.[88] This thermocouple has a thermoelectric power similar to chromel-alumel and is also stable at high temperature. High values of thermoelectric power have been found for interstitial graphite compounds, being as high as 50 μV/°C in some cases, but also a high thermal conductivity. (This would result in a low figure of merit for thermoelectric cooling. In addition, the materials are somewhat unstable and would probably suffer aging effects. As mentioned previously, superconductivity has also been measured on interstitial compounds,[76] but no effect was detected.

Summary and Conclusions

This chapter has been a brief review of the electrical properties of carbons and its crystal forms. An attempt has been made to define four situations where semiconduction exists, as well as instances where other electronic properties might be useful. Theoretical explanations of the electronic properties are difficult due to divergence of experimental results and poor characterization of samples. The application of carbon as an electronic material will never be of significance with the exception of electrodes and resistors. The principal value of studies in electronic properties at the present time is to indicate the similarity of these materials and their properties to organic semiconductors.

References

1. Mantell, C. L., "Industrial Carbon," Chapter I, New York, D. Van Nostrand, 1946.

2. Walker, P. L., Jr., "Advances in Catalysis," Vol. 11, p. 133, New York, Academic Press, 1959.
3. Grisdale, R. O., Pfister, A. C., and Van Roosbroek, W., *Bell Systems Tech. J.*, **30**, 271 (1951).
4. Walker, P. L., Jr., *American Scientist*, **50**, 259 (1962).
5. Boehm, H. P., and Hofmann, U., *Z. Anorg. Chem.*, **278**, 58 (1958).
6. Pinnick, H. T., Proceedings of the First and Second Conferences on Carbon, p. 1, Buffalo, N.Y., Univ. of Buffalo Press, 1956.
7. Kinney, C. R., Proceedings of the First and Second Conferences on Carbon, p. 83, Buffalo, N.Y., Univ. of Buffalo Press, 1956.
8. Franklin, R., *Acta Cryst.*, **4**, 253 (1951).
9. Private communication from High Temperature Materials, Inc., Boston, Mass.
10. Kotlensky, W. V., and Walker, P. L., Jr., Proceedings of the Fourth Conference on Carbon, p. 423, London, Pergamon Press, 1960.
11. Okada, K., and Takeuchi, Y., Proceedings of the Fourth Conference on Carbon, p. 657, London, Pergamon Press, 1960.
12. Blackman, L. C. F., *Research*, **13**, 441 (1960).
13. Collins, F. M., Proceedings of the Third Conference on Carbon, p. 659, London, Pergamon Press, 1959.
14. Schaeffer, W. D., Smith, W. R., Polley, M. H., *Ind. Eng. Chem.*, **45**, 1721 (1953).
15. Diefendorf, R. J., *J. chim. Phys.*, **57**, 815 (1960).
16. Geballe, T. H., "Semiconductors," p. 382, Ed. N. B. Hannay, New York, Reinhold, 1959.
17. Custers, J. F. H., *Physica*, **18**, 489 (1952).
18. Honda, H., Proceedings of the Third Conference on Carbon, p. 224, London, Pergamon Press, 1959.
19. Robertson, R., Fox, J. J., and Martin, A. F., *Phil. Trans. Royal Soc.*, **A232**, 463 (1934).
20. Dyer, H. B., and Wedepohl, P. T., *Proc. Phys. Soc.*, **69B**, 410 (1956).
21. Custers, J. F. H., *Physica*, **20**, 183 (1954).
22. Austin, I. G., and Wolfe, R., *Proc. Phys. Soc.*, **B69**, 329 (1956).
23. Mitchell, E. W. J., and Wedepohl, P. T., *Proc. Phys. Soc.*, **B70**, 527 (1957).
24. Kemmey, P. J., and Mitchell, E. W. J., *Proc. Roy. Soc.*, **263A**, 420 (1961).
25. Halperin, A., and Nahum, J., *J. Phys. and Chem. Solids*, **18**, 291 (1961).
26. Private Communication from M. H. Sirvetz and W. W. Oldfield, Jr., Hyletronics, Burlington, Massachusetts.
27. Primak, W., and Fuchs, L., *Phys. Rev.*, **95**, 22 (1954).
28. Dutta, A. K., *Phys. Rev.*, **90**, 187 (1953).
29. Primak, W., *Phys. Rev.*, **103**, 544 (1956).
30. Blackman, L. C. F., Matthews, J. F., and Ubbelohole, A. R., *Proc. Roy. Soc.*, **A256**, 15 (1960).
31. Breckindridge, R. J., Semiconductors and Phosphors, *Proc. Intern. Colloq.*, Garmisch-Partenkirchen, **1956**, 456 (1958); *C.A.* **54**, 7li (1960).
32. McClure, J. W., Proceedings of the Third Conference on Carbon, p. 179, London, Pergamon Press, 1959.
33. Soule, D. E., Proceedings of the Third Conference on Carbon, p. 203, London, Pergamon Press, 1959.

34. Mal'tsova, L. F., and Marmar, E. N., *Acad. Nauk, Ukr. SSR*, **2**, No. 1, 50 (1962); *C.A.* **56**, 1661g (1962).
35. Bhattacharyya, R., *Ind. J. Phys.*, **33**, 407 (1959); *C.A.* **54**, 7262c (1960).
36. Mrozowski, S., Proceedings of the Third Conference on Carbon, p. 495, London, Pergamon Press, 1959.
37. Mrozowski, S., and Chaberski, A., *Phys. Rev.*, **104**, 74 (1956).
38. Adamson, A. F., and Blaydon, H. E., Proceedings of the Third Conference on Carbon, p. 147, London, Pergamon Press, 1959.
39. Hennig, G. R., Proceedings of the First and Second Conferences on Carbon, p. 114, Buffalo, New York, Univ. of Buffalo Press, 1956.
40. Mrozowski, S., and Andrew, J. F., Proceedings of the Fourth Conference on Carbon, p. 207, London, Pergamon Press, 1960.
41. Ubbelohde, A. R., and Orr, J. C., *Nature*, **179**, 193 (1957).
42. Ubbelohde, A. R., Blackman, L. C. F., Dundas, P. H., *J. Soc. Chem. Ind.*, **1959**, 595 (1959).
43. Private Communication from Harvey, J., Clark, D., and Eastabrook, J. N., Royal Aircraft Establishment (Farnborough).
44. Guentert, O. J., and Prewitt, C. I., paper presented at the Annual Meeting of the American Physical Society, Detroit, Michigan, March, 1960.
45. Klein, C. A., paper presented at the Annual Meeting of the American Physical Society, Detroit, Michigan, March, 1960.
46. Graham, J. A., Brown, A. R. G., Watt, W., "Industrial Carbon and Graphite," p. 309, London, Soc. Chem. Ind., 1958.
47. Brown, A. R. G., and Watt, W., "Industrial Carbon and Graphite," p. 86, London, Soc. Chem. Ind., 1958.
48. Klein, C. A., Proceedings of the Fifth Conference on Carbon, Vol. II, London, Pergamon Press, (In Press).
49. Klein, C. A., *Phys. Rev.*, **123**, 1581 (1961).
50. Fishbach, D. B., *Phys. Rev.*, **123**, 1613 (1961).
51. Corbato, F. J., Proceedings of the Third Conference on Carbon, p. 173, London, Pergamon Press, 1959.
52. Haering, R. R., and Wallace, P. R., Proceedings of the Third Conference on Carbon, p. 183, London, Pergamon Press, 1959.
53. Uebersfield, J., and Erb, E., Proceedings of the Third Conference on Carbon, p. 103, London, Pergamon Press, 1959.
54. Papers No. 28-35, Fifth Conference on Carbon, University Park, Penna., (1961), Proceedings to be published by Pergamon Press, London, Vol. II, (In Press).
55. Mrozowski, S., Proceedings of the Fourth Conference on Carbon, p. 271, London, Pergamon Press, 1960.
56. Toyoda, H., *Tanso*, **2**, 224 (1952); *C.A.* **49**, 12951b (1955).
57. Weiss, D. E., *Australian J. Chem.*, **14**, 157 (1961).
58. Knispel, C. C., and Swinbourne, E. S., *Australian J. Chem.*, **11**, 433 (1958).
59. Dutta, A. K., and Chowdhury, A., *Indian J. Phys.*, **28**, 312 (1954); *C.A.*, **51**, 7781e (1957).
60. Toyoda, H., and Nagashima, M., *J. Phys. Soc. Japan*, **14**, 274 (1959); *C.A.* **53**, 14616e (1959).
61. Conroy, J. S., Slysh, R. S., Murphy, D. B. and Kinney, C. R., Proceed-

ings of the Third Conference on Carbon, p. 395, London, Pergamon Press, 1959.
62. Andrews, P. A., and Armington, A. F., to be published.
63. Ubbelohde, A. R., and Lewis, F. A., "Graphite and Its Crystalline Compounds," Oxford, Clarendon Press, 1960.
64. Hennig, G. R., Proceedings of the Fourth Conference on Carbon, p. 221, London, Pergamon Press, 1960.
65. Soule, D. E., Proceedings of the Fifth Conference on Carbon, Vol. 1, p. 13, London, Pergamon Press, 1962.
66. Albert, P., and Parisot, J., Proceedings of the Third Conference on Carbon, p. 467, London, Pergamon Press, 1959.
67. Ubbelohde, A. R., and Lewis, F. A., "Graphite and Its Crystalline Compounds," p. 13, Oxford, Clarendon Press, 1960.
68. Hobstetter, J. N., "Semiconductors," p. 508, Ed. N. B. Hannay, New York, Reinhold, 1959.
69. Croft, R. C., Proceedings of the Third Conference on Carbon, p. 315, London, Pergamon Press, 1959.
70. Ubbelohde, A. R., and Lewis, F. A., "Graphite and Its Crystalline Compounds," Chap. 7, p. 143, Oxford, Clarendon Press, 1960.
71. Hennig, G. R., *J. Chem. Phys.*, **19**, 922 (1951).
72. Ubbelohde, A. R., Proceedings of the Third Conference on Carbon, p. 329, London, Pergamon Press, 1959.
73. McDonnell, F. R. M., Pick, R. C., and Ubbelohde, A. R., *J. Chem. Soc.*, **1951**, 191 (1951).
74. Hennig, G. R., *J. Chem. Phys.*, **20**, 1443 (1952).
75. Blackman, L. C. F., Dundas, P. H., Ubbelohde, A. R., *Proc. Royal Soc.*, **A255**, 293 (1960).
76. Hennig, G. R., *Phys. Rev.*, **87**, 439 (1952).
77. Setton, R., and Bazin, J., *Compte Rend.*, **254**, 2150 (1962).
78. Myers, I. T., and Larson, H. V., Proceedings of the Fifth Conference on Carbon, Vol. 2, London, Pergamon Press (In Press).
79. Blackman, L. C. F., *Proc. Phys. Soc.*, **78**, 1048 (1961).
80. Montet, G. L., Proceedings of the Fourth Conference on Carbon, p. 159, London, Pergamon Press, 1960.
81. Grenall, A., and Sosin, A., Proceedings of the Fourth Conference on Carbon, p. 371, London, Pergamon Press, 1960.
82. Ubbelohde, A. R., and Lewis, F. A., "Graphite and Its Crystalline Compounds," p. 9, Oxford, Clarendon Press, 1960.
83. Tsuzuku, T., Proceedings of the Fourth Conference on Carbon, p. 403, London, Pergamon Press, 1960.
84. Williamson, G. K., and Baker, C., Proceedings of the Fifth Conference on Carbon, Vol. 2, London, Pergamon Press, (In Press).
85. Bacon, R., and Sprague, R., Proceedings of the Fifth Conference on Carbon, Vol. I, p. 466, London, Pergamon Press, 1962.
86. Gulbransen, E. A., Andrew, K. F., *Ind. Eng. Chem.*, **44**, 1034 (1952).
87. Shepard, R. L., Pattin, H. S., and Westbrook, R. D., *Bull. Am. Phys. Soc.* (*2*), **1**, 119 (1956).
88. Medcalf, W. E., and Fahrig, R. H., *J. Electrochem. Soc.*, **105**, 719 (1958).

7

Polymers

Semiconducting Polymers

In general organic macromolecular materials have been considered in terms of good electrical insulators with many important industrial applications based on the proper utilization of these properties. These have been attributed to the characteristics of the carbon-carbon bonding system. It has been known for a long time, however, that certain graphitic and other carbon containing structures do show an appreciable amount of electronic conduction. More recent experimental investigations have developed sufficient data to indicate that suitably designed organic polymer structures are not necessarily insulators. It now appears feasible to consider the synthesis of special macromolecular structures with a wide range of electronic conduction characteristics.

The investigation of the electronic properties of organic high molecular weight materials presents a number of special problems to the researcher. These arise to a large extent from the peculiarities of the materials being studied. Most polymers contain molecules of varying molecular weights. The relationship between molecular weight and conductivity has as yet not been quantitatively determined, although it has been the subject of some speculation for certain specific polymer structures. Also catalysts, modifiers, etc., are widely used in the preparation of most polymers. Many of them are highly conductive metals—often in finely divided form—or contain significant amounts of metallic compounds. Such inorganic impurities may significantly affect the electrical conductivity. Furthermore, there may be present possible organic impurities which could also influence polymer conductivities and/or other electronic properties.

It is becoming apparent, therefore, that studies of the electronic behavior of organic high molecular weight substances are likely to require special polymer preparatory methods as well as effective purification techniques and, if possible, the availability of the material being evaluated in a narrow molecular weight range. Unfortunately, however, most of the experimental studies which have been carried out on this subject, have not employed such precautionary measures. The results obtained are, therefore, open to some discussion. A re-evaluation of currently available information as well as extension of this knowledge to develop pertinent relationships between conductivity and polymer structure are only two of the many immediate needs in this field.

In polyethylene, each bond is formed by a pair of electrons. Theoretical calculations indicate that the energy to remove these electrons is very high. However, if adjacent hydrogen atoms are removed, a series of conjugated double bonds is formed. The orbitals of the electrons forming such conjugated polymer bonding systems are much further away from the carbon nuclei and, thus, the electrons should be more easily removed. As the number of double bonds, i.e., the chain length, increases, the bonding energy of these electrons becomes lower. A major reason for this loss of the bonding energy of these electrons is due to resonance phenomena caused by overlapping of the eigenfunctions for these various bonds. Calculations have been made based on potential energies involved. They indicate that long chains of conjugated double bonds may possess near metallic conductivity characteristics.

In such conjugated chain structures large numbers of electrons cause a decrease of the internal energy as well as a decrease of the excitation energy of the π electrons. Currently available experimental data appear to confirm, to a certain extent, that the properties of polymers with conjugated bonds depend at least in part on the length and the structure of the chains. Also, the character of any lateral groups or the presence of certain heteroatoms in the chains can affect electronic properties.

Various preparative schemes have been experimentally investigated for the synthesis of polymeric materials with conjugated chains. These include the following:

(a) Polymerization of acetylenic (triple bond) compounds.

(b) Intermolecular elimination of pertinent atoms or molecules by dehydrogenation, dehydrohalogenation, etc.

(c) Polycondensations.

(d) Syntheses involving chelate compounds.

Polymerization of Triple Bond Compounds

The polymerization of triple bond containing chemical compounds appears to offer a particularly attractive route on account of its apparent simplicity. It has, therefore, been the subject of a considerable amount of research and development for the preparation of macromolecular conjugated bonding systems. The polymerizations of compounds containing triple bonds are shown below as follows:

$$nR-C\equiv C-R' \rightarrow \left[\begin{array}{c} -C=C- \\ | \quad | \\ R \quad R' \end{array} \right]_n$$

$$nR-C\equiv N \rightarrow \left[\begin{array}{c} -C=N- \\ | \\ R \end{array} \right]_n$$

Typical polymerization techniques which have been studied for such preparations include the bulk, solution and suspension methods. A limited amount of research has also been concerned with the choice of suitable polymerization initiators. Catalysts which have been employed for effecting triple bond polymerization reactions range from modified Ziegler-Natta systems to high energy irradiations and high pressures as well as heat alone.

Acetylene has of course been of special interest here because its polymerizates could be in the form of high molecular weight conjugated chains. An acetylene polymer called cuprene[1] has been known for over thirty years. Cuprene is prepared in the presence of copper catalysts or by heating. Electrical conduction charac-

teristics of this apparently at least partially cross linked polyacetylene have as yet not been ascertained.

More recently Natta,[2] Luttinger,[3] Green,[4] Hatano,[5] Watson,[6] and
others have investigated acetylene polymerizations in considerable
detail. Natta, *et al.*, have produced highly crystalline, generally
insoluble and infusible polyacetylenes using variously modified
Ziegler-Natta type of catalyst systems. The polymerization products were dark brown or black in color.

Acetylene polymerization catalysts comprising nickel and cobalt
salts or their complexes with sodium borohydride have been ad-
vocated by Luttinger.[3] Their dark colored polymerization products
are said to be generally similar to the Natta developed materials.

Green, *et al.*, have studied catalyst systems containing trimethyl-
phosphine, etc.[4] A communication of these workers confirms the
insolubility, infusibility, and high thermal stability of these acetylenic polymers.

Watson and his co-workers have employed modified Ziegler
catalysts for the polymerization of various acetylene compounds.
Specifically, acetylene, propyne, and butyne-1 have been polymerized with catalysts comprised of aluminum triisobutyl, *n*-butyl
lithium, or zinc diethyl in combination with titanium tetrachloride.
The conductivity measurements of the colored polyacetylenes
produced showed typical semiconductor behavior (10^{-4} ohm^{-1}-cm^{-1}
at 25°C).

Hatano and his co-workers have employed modified Ziegler
catalysts for the polymerization of acetylene.[5] Polymerizations
were conducted at a wide range of temperatures under strictly
anhydrous conditions. Some properties of acetylene polymerization
products are summarized in Table 7-1.

These polyacetylenes were also black or dark in color, insoluble,
and infusible. Microanalysis showed that when tested they contained rather significant amounts of oxygen. The oxygen contents
increased with prolonged storage in air at ambient temperature.
It has, therefore, been considered that the polyacetylenes were
gradually oxidized by air. Typically the oxygen contents increased
to 23 weight per cent after 15 days in storage at ambient temperature.

Experimental data show that the energy gap of crystalline poly-

Table 7-1. Paramagnetic and Electric Properties of Polyacetylene.[5]

Catalyst Composition	Ratio	Temperature, °C	Solvent	Conc. of Unpaired Electrons, Spin/g	Elect. Resist., ohm-cm (25°C)	Crystallinity
$Al(C_2H_5)_3/TiCl_4$	1:2:1	16–18	n-heptane	4.3×10^{18}	—	amorphous
$Al(C_2H_5)_3/TiCl_4$	1:2:1	16–18	n-heptane	4.4×10^{18}	3.7×10^9	amorphous
$Al(C_2H_5)_3/TiCl_4$	1:2:1	−70	n-heptane	11×10^{18}	1.6×10^8	low cryst.
$Al(C_2H_5)_3/Ti(OC_4H_9)_4$	2:1	0	toluene	36×10^{18}	4.2×10^5	medium cryst.
$Al(C_2H_5)_3/Ti(OC_4H_9)_4$	2:1	80	toluene	47×10^{18}	1.4×10^4	highly cryst.

acetylenes is lower than that of amorphous polyacetylenes. The crystalline polyacetylenes had an energy gap of 0.23 eV as against 0.42 eV for amorphous materials. It has been suggested that this is due to the presence of longer conjugated systems in the crystalline polymer modifications.

The infusibility and insolubility of acetylene polymers has prompted a number of other polymerization studies with acetylenic monomers which might be expected to produce more tractable macromolecular systems. Of special interest is a linear poly-phenylacetylene structure $\left[\begin{array}{c} -C{=}CH- \\ | \\ Ph \end{array} \right]_n$ in which the alternating phenyl rings and conjugated double bonds create a decrease in the system's internal energy and apparently allow electron transfer for electronic conduction. Phenyl acetylene monomer can be conveniently prepared from β-bromostyrene with potassium hydroxide. It is a colorless liquid with a boiling point of 143°C.

Phenyl acetylene monomer has been polymerized in various ways. Korshak,[7] et al., have employed peroxide initiators at 70° to 200°C under 1 to 6000 atmospheres pressure. Comparatively low yields (3 to 60 per cent) of products of unknown structure were obtained. The products were initially brittle orange-red solids which became yellow powders on reprecipitation from benzene. Berlin[8] has polymerized phenyl acetylene monomer both thermally and catalytically. He obtained yellow solids having a high degree of thermal stability and exhibiting comparative inertness in addition reactions. The assumed structure was that of a conjugated polyvinyline, based solely on experimental evidence of chemical inactivity and E.S.R. spectra showing unpaired electrons.

The polymerization of phenyl acetylene monomer has also been attempted with modified heterogeneous catalyst systems of the type used in olefin polymerization reactions. Champetier and Martynoff[9] have obtained presumably the same type of polymers by using organomagnesium compounds in the presence of ferric chloride or titanium tetrachloride. Again the yields were low and the structures were not identified.

A more recent study by Okamoto, et al.,[10] showed that phenylacetylene monomer can be polymerized thermally quite easily at temperatures of 150 to 200°C. Near quantitative yields were obtained either in bulk (absence of solvents) or in 10 to 20 weight per cent solutions of selected hydrocarbon solvents. Yellow and dark colored products with molecular weights of 500 to 1000 were obtained. Their room temperature resistivity and energy gap were determined to be 10^{16} ohm cm and 0.96 eV, respectively. The conjugated nature of these polymer structures was determined by hydrogenation to polystyrene. Efforts were also made to prepare higher molecular weight phenylacetylene polymers by using modified Ziegler-Natta catalyst systems and high energy ionizing radiation. The modified Ziegler-Natta catalyst system produced only cyclic trimerization products.

Stille, et al., have polymerized 1,6-heptadiyne using a Ziegler type catalyst system.[11] The room temperature resistivity of poly 1,6-heptadiyne, whose assumed structure is shown in Figure 7-1,

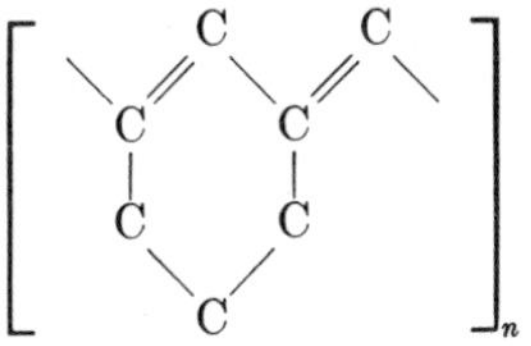

Figure 7-1. Poly-1,6-heptadiyne.

was found to be in the 10^{10} to 10^{13} ohm-cm range. This rather high resistance may be due to the relative instability of this polymer with reagents and air, thus breaking the conjugated chains.

A limited amount of experimental work has also been carried out on the polymerization of nitriles. It has been found that acrylonitrile when exposed to γ rays at —78°C in ethylene[12] produces a small amount of a polymer of the structure

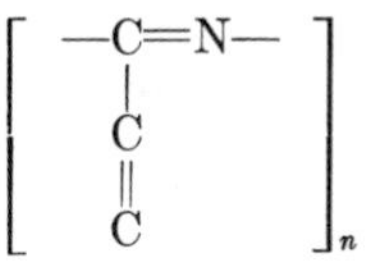

In bulk of course, the conventional polyacrylonitrile

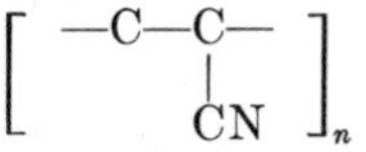

is obtained. However, no conductivity measurements have been reported for the former polymer.

The polymerization of aromatic nitriles has been investigated as well. The preparation of 1,3,5-triazenes from aromatic mononitriles, such as benzonitrile is known.[13,14,15] The polymerization may be catalytic or conducted in the absence of catalyst employing heat and pressure. Various catalyst systems have been described,[16] such as small amounts of copper, manganese, or cobalt halides or acetates. Electrical properties have not been determined.

Higher molecular weight materials (linear polymerization products) have as yet not been obtained, but such preparations might prove to be of definite interest in this field. Further work along these lines may help elucidate the characteristics of —C≡N— bonding systems.

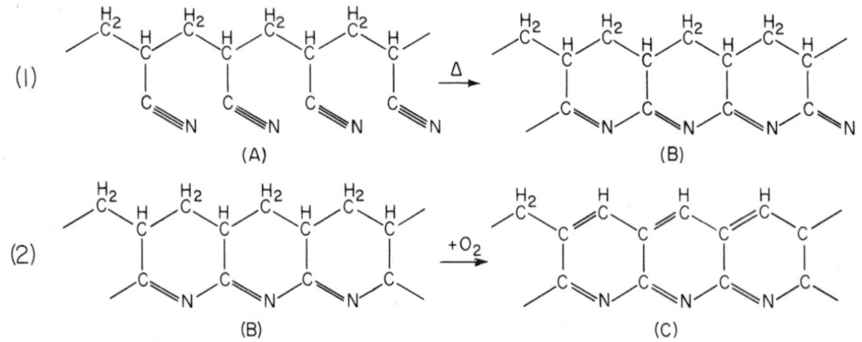

Figure 7-2. Thermal conversion of polyacrylonitrile.

A considerable amount of research and development has been carried out on the thermal conversions of polyacrylonitrile. Polyacrylonitrile fibers are readily available under the trade names "Orlon" (E. I. DuPont Co.) and "Acrilan" (Chemstrand). It was observed some time ago in the DuPont laboratories that when "Orlon" fibers were heated in air above 160°C, "an exothermic reaction took place resulting in the formation of a black fireproof textile which retained upwards of 40 per cent of the initial fabric tenacity. This material was called "AF."[17,18]

AF fibers prepared by heat treating "Orlon" polyacrylonitrile fibers in air above 160°C are fireproof, quite resistant to intense short time thermal irradiations, and maintain significant strength properties at surprisingly high temperatures for limited time periods. At 900°C for example, they have some strength retention for upward of two hours. The structural changes which are believed to occur upon the thermal conversion of polyacrylonitrile have been depicted as follows:[17,19,20,21]

The above thermal conversion should, therefore, result in structures such as (C) which contain conjugated double bonds as well as regularly alternating nitrogen atoms each having a pair of electrons which do not form a chemical bond. This suggests possible semiconductor properties for such polymers. Topchiyev and co-workers have reported that significant conductivity can be obtained in thermally converted polyacrylonitriles.[22]

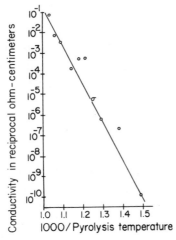

Figure 7-3. Room temperature resistivity characteristics of pyrolized polyacrylonitrile samples as a function of inverse pyrolysis temperature.

Brennan and his co-workers[23] have conducted quite detailed studies of the electrical conductivity, Hall effect, and thermoelectric characteristics of pyrolyzed polyacrylonitrile samples. The pyrolysis temperatures ranged from 400 to 900°C in a nitrogen atmosphere. The Hall constant was found to be less than 0.1 cc/coulomb in at least one sample. For all specimens, the forbidden energy gap was close to 0.1 eV and the mobility ratio was close to unity.

The resistivity data of Brennan, et al., are summarized in Figure 7-3. The room temperature resistivities are shown to be an inverse function of the pyrolysis temperature. This can of course be associated with an increase in the number of conjugated sites on the polymer when it has been subjected to greater pyrolysis temperatures. The value of the energy gap may also be related to electron activation within the conjugated structure.

Geiderikh, et al.,[24] have also studied the thermal conversion products of polyacrylonitrile. The measured values of the activation energy and electrical conductivity of pyrolyzed polyacrylonitrile samples ranged from 0.05 to 0.32 eV and 10^{-10} to 10^{-3} ohm^{-1} cm^{-1} at ambient temperatures. No Hall effect values could be obtained which result in conflicts with data of other investigators.[23] This discrepancy may be due to the very low mobility of the current carriers.

The thermal treatment of polyacrylonitrile under ammonia pressure has been reported to result in a marked increase in electroconductivity as well as noticeable reductions of the activation energy.[24]

A main problem in studies of thermally converted polyacrylonitriles is the still basically unknown structure of these materials. The nature of the pyrolysis reactions is such that end products exhibiting significant variations in structure, properties, etc., can be expected. Such variations are likely to be reflected in turn in inconsistent measurements of pertinent solid state properties.

The theoretically assumed structure of thermally converted polyacrylonitriles remains, however, one of continued interest. The development of a direct preparative method for such a highly conjugated nitrogen containing polymer could indeed be of considerable help towards a better understanding of electrical conduction phenomena in such polymeric organic systems.

Intermolecular Elimination of Pertinent Atoms or Molecules by Dehydrogenation, Dehydrohalogenation, Etc.

The elimination of atoms and molecules from polymeric structures to produce materials with significantly different properties has been the subject of a substantial amount of experimental investigations for a considerable period of time. The intramolecular abstraction of atoms and molecules from saturated molecules has been of particularly interest for both theoretical and practical reasons. Polyvinylalcohol and polyvinyl halides and esters have been studied in much detail both for the prevention and the promotion of such elimination reactions. In certain cases such elimination reactions have been associated with the occurrence of thermal or light initiated and promoted degradation phenomena.

Grassie[25] describes a most common type of elimination reaction as follows:

$$
\left[\begin{array}{c} \text{H} \quad \text{X} \\ | \quad | \\ -\text{C}-\text{C}- \\ | \quad | \\ \text{H} \quad \text{Y} \end{array} \right]_n \rightarrow \left[\begin{array}{c} \text{H} \quad \text{Y} \\ | \quad | \\ -\text{C}=\text{C}- \\ \end{array} \right]_n + \text{HX}
$$

where X is Cl, Br, OH, CH_3—C—O—, etc.
$$\parallel$$
$$\text{O}$$

The polymeric system most studied is probably polyvinylchloride which is known to give off small amounts of hydrochloric acid when exposed to high environmental temperatures without adequate stabilization. The dehalogenation of polyvinyl chloride has been carried out with zinc, lithium aluminum hydride, etc. Reduction of polyvinylchloride with zinc or lithium aluminum hydride does not yield structures with conjugated unsaturation.[26]

Halogens can also be removed from a polyvinylhalide by treatment with alkalis. The elimination of bromine in the form of hydrogen bromide is brought about particularly readily. Treatment of polyvinylbromide with alcoholic solutions of alkalis, organic bases, or ammonia results in the formation of dark-colored polyvinylenes which frequently show only little solubility and flow properties in sharp contrast with the unmodified polymers. Resistivity measurements of such polyvinylenes show a decrease of resistivity at higher temperatures which conforms to semiconductive behavior.[27]

Hydrogen chloride has been removed from commercially produced polyvinylidene chloride by treatment with boiling morpholine or alcoholic alkali solutions in a nitrogen atmosphere. Elemental analysis showed that the product generally had the desired structure but contained a substantial amount of oxidized material. The conductivity characteristics were found to be significantly enhanced, particularly at elevated temperatures. Bohrer measured a resistivity of 10^{10} ohm-cm at 100°C. The energy gap was 0.87 eV.[28]

Winslow and co-workers[29] have investigated elimination reactions in considerable detail. Thermal conversion products of polyvinyledine chloride and preoxidized divinylbenzene exhibited definite paramagnetic absorption. The products of such pyrolytic

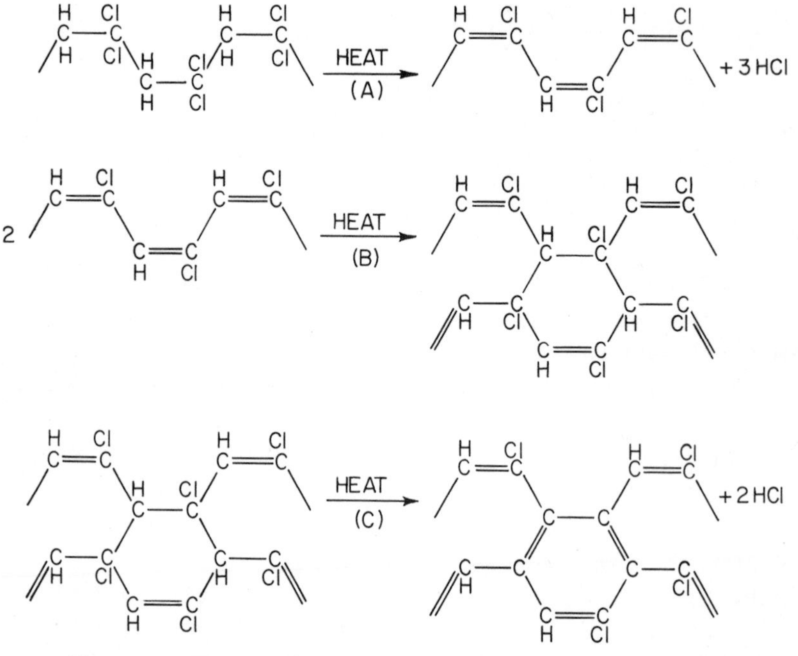

Figure 7-4. Thermal degradation of polyvinyledine chloride.

treatments have been termed "polymer" carbons. The degradation of polyvinyledine chloride is quite complex particularly in the advanced stages. The initial elimination of hydrochloric acid has been attributed to a zip reaction A that produces a linear polyacetylene by successive release of adjacent hydrochloric acid groups along the polymer chain. A Diels-Alder reaction B satisfies the stepwise decomposition, and the formation of polyene rings may follow C.

During the various stages of the pyrolysis reactions, the x-ray diagrams of the heat treated products changed from amorphous to

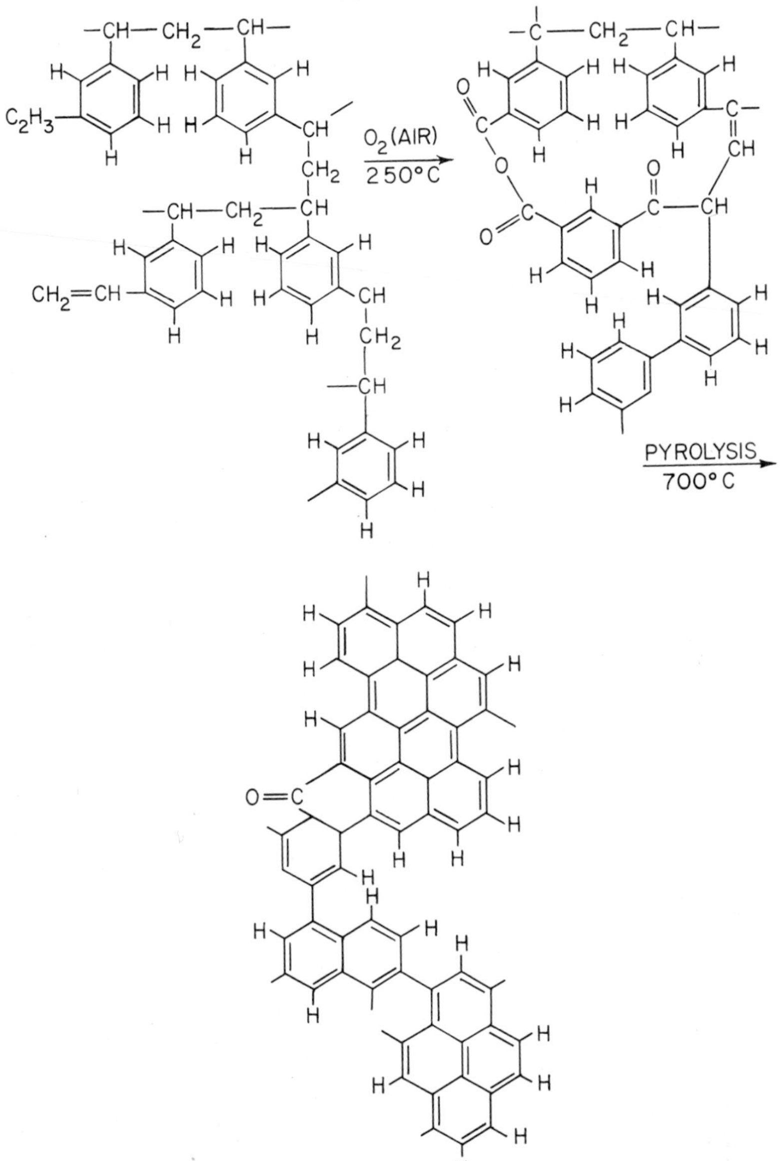

Figure 7-5. Schematic conversion of divinylbenzene polymer to a carbon-like semiconductor.

steadily more crystalline patterns. This suggests that a polycyclic aromatic network with little if any aliphatic bonding exists above 500°C. A schematic conversion of divinylbenzene to polymer carbon was suggested as in Figure 7-5.

Divinylbenzene polymer is initially highly crosslinked and may have entrapped radicals and residual vinyl groups. The oxidation disrupts and removes much of the aliphatic portion of the polymer. Extensive dehydrogenation and rearrangement occurs accompanied by increases in conjugation and crosslinking. Between 400 and 600°C, condensation and rearrangement occurs quite rapidly with large loss of volatiles. The d-c resistivities of the polymer increase markedly when the pyrolysis temperature exceeds 600°C, as shown in Table 7-2.[30]

Table 7-2. Electrical Resistivities of Pyrolysis Products from Pre-oxidized Polydivinylbenzene.[30]

Pyrolysis Temp., °C	Empirical Formula of Residues	Resistivity,* ohm-cm, 25°C
500	$C_{22}H_{17}O$	10^{15}
600	$C_{34}H_{13}O$	10^{12}
700	$C_{45}H_{16}O$	10^6
1000	~0.6% H	10^{-2}

* Resistivity measurements made on pressure molded pellets.

Polycondensations

The preparation of linear conjugated condensed polyaromatics has been of interest because such structures have been expected to

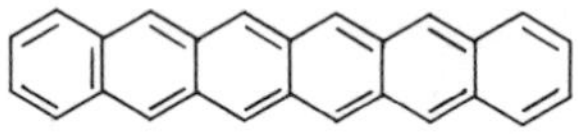

Figure 7-6. Hexacene.

show significant electronic conduction. Syntheses are difficult, however, because the peri hydrogens are rather easily oxidized. One of the longer chain which has been prepared is hexacene[31,32] (Figure 7-6). Electronic properties of hexacene have been measured.[33] The resistivity and the activation energy are $\rho_{50°} = 3 \times 10^{10}$ ohm cm and $E = 0.57eV$.

Polyphenyl compounds have also been considered. The compound p-terphenyl has been studied as a single crystal.[34] A room temperature resistivity of 10^{14} ohm-cm has been reported. The energy gap was found to be 0.60 eV. p-Sexiphenyl was synthesized by Ullman's reaction as shown in Figure 7-7.[35] The electronic properties of this dark brown compound which is insoluble in many common organic solvents and does not melt at 550°C, have been determined. (see Chapter 4).

Marvel and Hartzell have attempted to prepare longer polyphenyl chains by the Ziegler catalyzed polymerication of dihydrobenzene followed by dehydration.[36] (See Figure 7-8.)

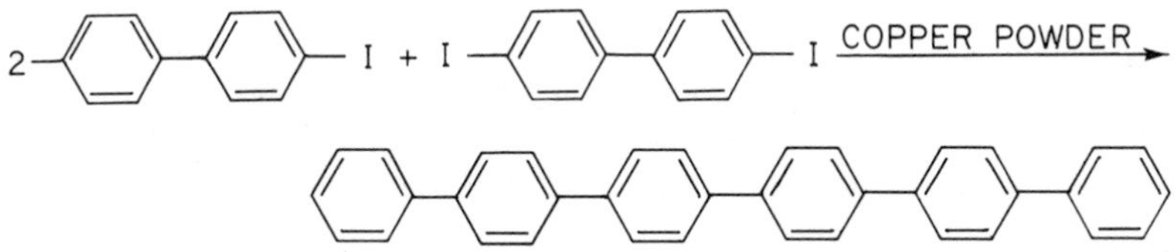

Figure 7-7. Preparation of p-sexiphenyl.

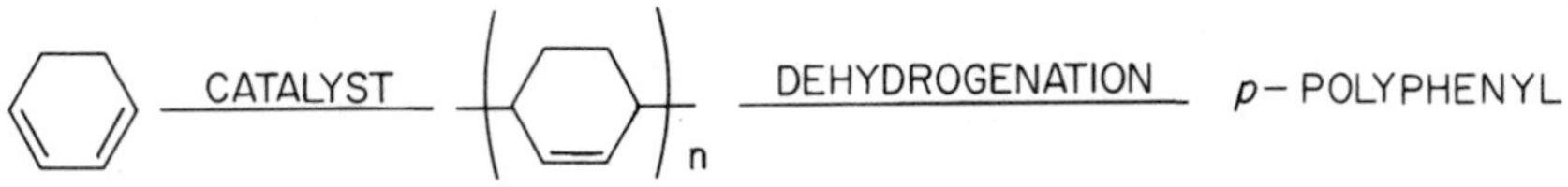

Figure 7-8. Polymerization of dihydrobenzene.

Also Edward and Goldfinger[37] have studied the synthesis of a considerable number of long chain polyphenyls by the Wurtz-Fittig reaction. Polymers containing up to approximately 34 benzene rings were obtained. Itoh[38] has obtained similar reaction products and determined a specific resistivity of 6×10^{10} ohm-cm at ambient temperatures for the 34 ring containing polyphenyl.[38]

The polymerization of benzene has been recently accomplished by Kovacic and Kyriakis.[39] Friedel-Craft type catalysis using aluminum and cupric chlorides proved effective for the preparation of para polyphenyls. It was considered that a minor amount of cross links may be present in these polymers. The resistivity of such polymers was determined as $\rho_{50}° = 6 \times 10^{14}$ ohm-cm (see Chapter 4).

When aromatic hydrocarbons are heated with an excess of sulfur in sealed tubes *in vacuo* up to 450°C dark-colored sulfur containing compounds have been obtained.[40] The following structure has been suggested for the anthracene-sulfur compound whose room temperature resistivity and energy gaps were measured as 10^2 to 10^4

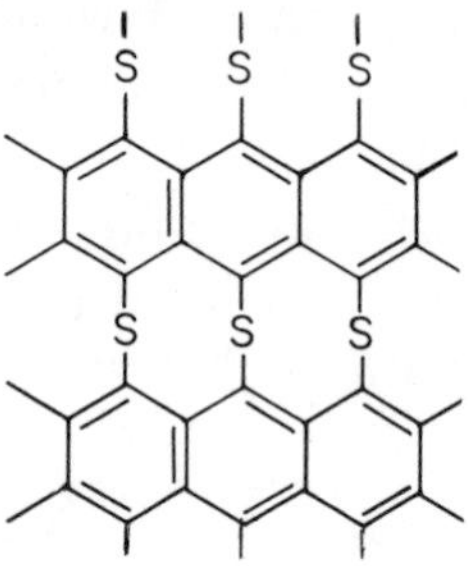

Figure 7-9. Anthracene: suggested structure for sulfur compounds.

ohm-cm and 0.4 eV, respectively. (See Figure 7-9.) A compilation of the properties of these sulfur containing polyaromatics is shown in Table 7-3.

Table 7-3. Electronic Properties and Sulfur Content of Sulfur-Containing Polyaromatic Compounds.[40]

Hydrocarbon	Resistivity $\rho 50°C$ ohm-cm	Energy Gap E, eV	Sulfur Content Number of Sulfur Atoms per Hydrocarbon Molecule
Anthracene	1.0×10^4	0.09	5.8
Tetracene	1.4×10^4	0.075	7.1
Perylene	2.0×10^9	0.29	8.6
Pyranthrene	5.0×10^3	0.11	11.5
Violanthrene	1.1×10^4	0.10	9.7
Violanthrone	4.0×10^2	0.08	9.5

Polyphenylazocompounds have been prepared by Berlin and other Russian workers.[41,42,43] Diazotization reactions were employed as shown in Figure 7-10. The polymers were found to possess large magnetic susceptibility constants $\chi = 0.50 \times 10^{-6}$ and 10^{17}–10^{19} spins per gram of free electrons.

Marvel and Vogel[44] have prepared polybenzimidazoles by the following route. The electronic properties have apparently not been measured (see Figure 7-11.)

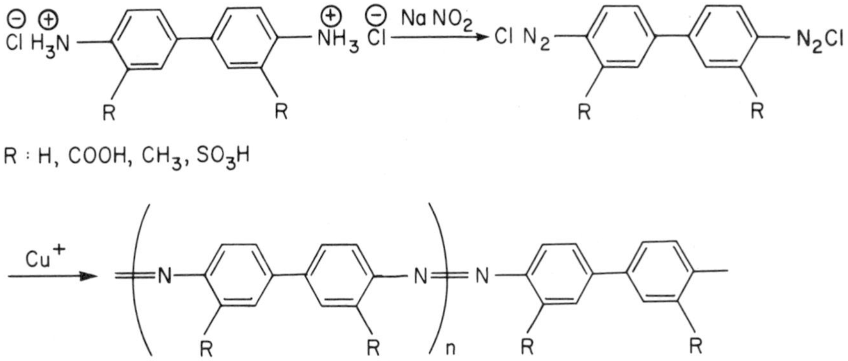

R : H, COOH, CH₃, SO₃H

Figure 7-10. Preparation of polyphenylazo compounds.

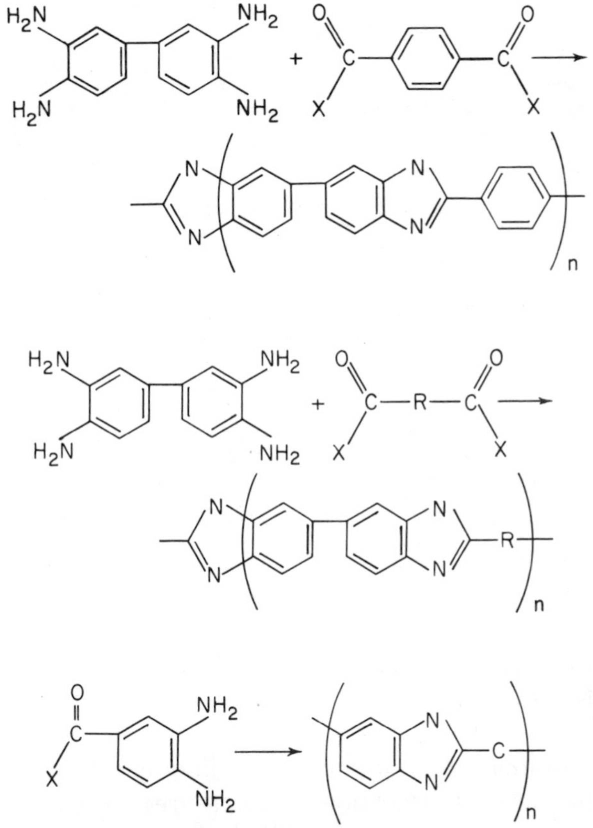

Figure 7-11. Preparation of polybenzimidazoles.

Other potentially interesting novel polymer structures have been synthesized by Lenz[45] and Marvel.[46] The preparative routes are shown in Figure 7-12.

Geiderikh and co-workers[24] have condensed phthalic anhydride

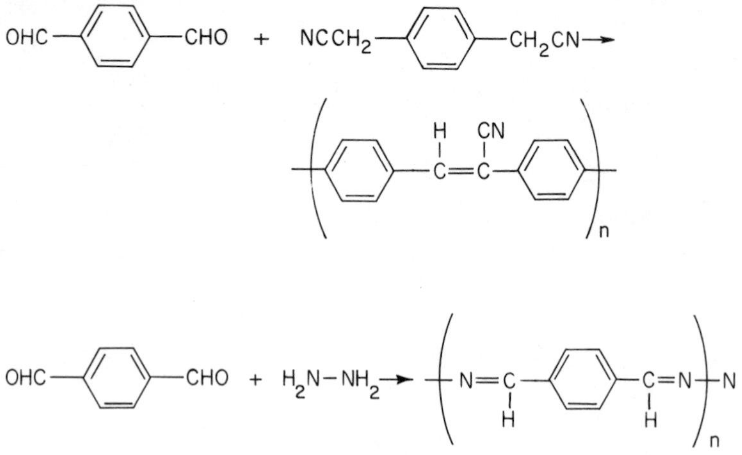

Figure 7-12. Preparation of azine polymers.

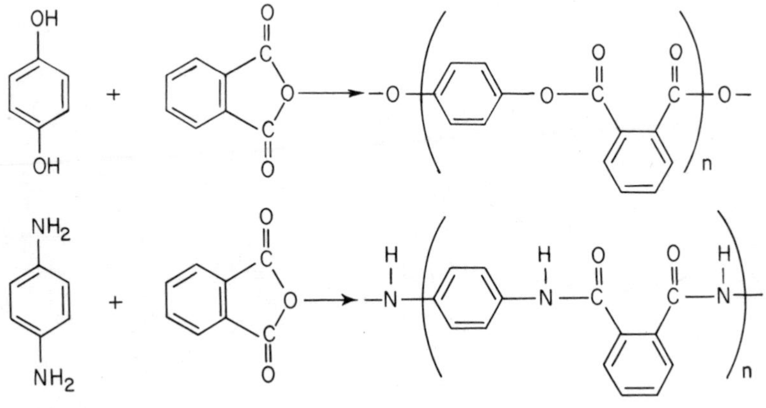

Figure 7-13. Polycondensation of phthalic anhydride with hydroquinone and p-phenylene diamine.

with hydroquinone and p-phenylene diamine. Zinc chloride was used as the catalyst. Reaction temperatures were reported to be 250°C. The results are shown in Figure 7-13 and Table 7-4.

The recently reported synthesis of polymeric aromatic com-

Table 7-4. Electronic Properties of Phthalate Polymers.

	Number of Electrons with Unpaired Spins per Gram	Conductivity at 20°C, ohm^{-1} cm^{-1}	E Activat. Energy, eV
Phthalic anhydride-hydroquinone condensate	5.9×10^{19}	7×10^{-7}	0.58
Phthalic anhydride-hydroquinone-glycerin condensate	7.8×10^{19}	2×10^{-7}	0.55

pounds which contain quinone and amino groups in the chain of conjugation, is of considerable interest. Their suggested structure is as shown in Figure 7-14. Berlin and co-workers[43] have established that these polyaminoquinones have activation energies of 0.5–0.6 eV. Magnetic susceptibility constants were ~ 1.3 × 10^{-6}.

McNeill and Weiss[47] have reacted resorcinol with phthalic anhydride in the presence of catalysts such as zinc chloride. Reaction

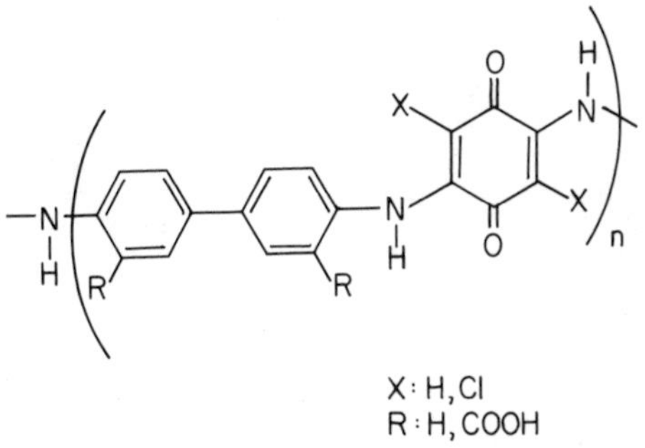

X: H, Cl
R: H, COOH

Figure 7-14. Polyphenylene diaminoquinones.

temperatures ranged up to 200°C. The products are thought to be similar to xanthene dyestuffs. They were black tars, soluble in alkali but insoluble in ethanol.

More insoluble polymers were obtained by replacing phthalic anhydride with an anhydride of greater functionality, such as pyromelletic dianhydride. The substitution of resorcinol for hydroquinone brings about a completely insoluble xanthene polymer. A suggested structure is shown in Figure 7-15. This polymer is a *p*-

type semiconductor with a specific resistance as low as 7×10^3 ohm-cm.

Pohl and his co-workers have carried out similar investigations. The preparation of more than sixty polymers has been reported by the Friedel-Crafts reaction of various aromatic hydrocarbon compounds with aromatics and anhydrides in the presence of zinc chloride.[48] The polymers obtained were generally hard, black, insoluble, and infusible materials and contained a high content of

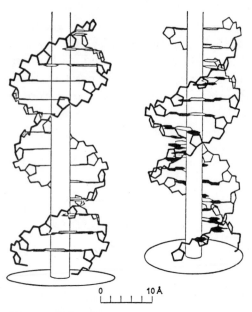

Figure 7-15. Suggested structure of the xanthene polymer.

free radicals. Pohl has called them polyacene quinone radical polymers (PAQR).

The resistivities were measured as compacted powders using a d-c method. The powders were compacted at pressures in the order of 2500 kg/cm² because there was found to be little if any resistivity pressure dependency at these pressure levels. Resistivity measurements are summarized in Table 7-5.

Engelhardt[49] has reacted aromatic hydrocarbons and aromatic acid anhydrides to produce polymeric compounds which are

Table 7-5. Room Temperature Resistivities of Polyacene Quinone Radical Polymers, ρ.

Polymerization Temp., °C	1,8-Naphthalic Anhydride		Pyromellitic Anhydride		Phthalic Anhydride	Tetraphenyl 1,2-dihydro-phthatic Anhydride
	256	306	256	306	256	306
1,2-Dihydroxyanthraquinone	3.2×10^7	1.7×10^7	2.3×10^7	—	2.3×10^8	—
1,4-Dihydroxyanthraquinone	1.0×10^7	—	—	—	—	—
1,5-Dihydroxyanthraquinone	3.3×10^6	7.0×10^5	7.0×10^9	1.4×10^7	3.1×10^5	—
1,8-Dihydroxyanthraquinone	1.7×10^5	3.2×10^4	9.0×10^6	4.8×10^7	1.4×10^9	1.9×10^6
2,7-Dihydroxynaphthalene	5.1×10^5	—	5.2×10^{10}	1.5×10^7	1.3×10^7	—
1,4-Dihydroxynaphthalene	4.4×10^{10}	3.9×10^5	8.4×10^9	2.5×10^8	2.1×10^7	—
1-Bromo-2-naphthol	3.2×10^6	—	4.1×10^6	—	2.6×10^6	—
6-Bromo-2-naphthol	5.8×10^5	—	1.6×10^6	—	1.5×10^6	—
Phenolphthalein	1.1×10^6	—	2.0×10^8	—	2.9×10^9	—
9-Bromophenanthrene	5.6×10^6	4.1×10^5	—	—	2.0×10^9	—
1,4-Bisanthraquinonylamino-anthraquinone	—	1.6×10^5	—	4.1×10^6	—	—
1,4,9,10-Tetrahydroxyanthracene	7.1×10^5	—	—	—	1.2×10^5	—
Dibenzanthrone (violanthrone)	1.0×10^6	—	1.9×10^8	—	—	—
7-Acenaphthol	1.2×10^8	—	1.8×10^7	—	2.1×10^6	—
Carbazole	2.6×10^8	—	—	—	1.6×10^7	—
1-Hydroxyanthraquinone	4.7×10^6	8.3×10^4	—	7.0×10^5	1.4×10^6	—
p-Naphtholbenzein	3.3×10^{10}	—	—	—	4.7×10^6	—
2-Bromo-4-phenylphenol	4.9×10^{10}	—	—	—	6.9×10^7	—
p,p'-Diphenol	—	—	—	—	2.6×10^{10}	—

145

Table 7-5. Room Temperature Resistivities of Polyacene Quinone Radical Polymers, ρ. (Continued)

Polymerization Temp., °C	1,8-Naphthalic Anhydride		Pyromellitic Anhydride		Phthalic Anhydride	Tetraphenyl 1,2-dihydro-phthalic Anhydride
	256	306	256	306	256	306
1,4-Diphenyl piperazein	2.0×10^5	—	—	—	1.2×10^{11}	—
Anthraquinone	9.9×10^5	—	1.3×10^5	—	5.0×10^4	—
Phenol (3PA + 4 phenol)	2.2×10^8	—	2.6×10^9	—	1.6×10^7	—
Phenol (1A + 2 phenol)	5.9×10^9	—	3.6×10^{10}	—	2.2×10^7	—
1,4-Naphthoquinone	2.4×10^{10}	—	2.0×10^{11}	—	9.4×10^{10}	—
1,4-Diaminoanthraquinone	1.2×10^6	—	2.6×10^7	—	—	—
p-Quinone	7.5×10^9	—	9.0×10^9	—	2.4×10^{11}	—
			22×10^{10}			
2-Methylanthraquinone	—	—	5.2×10^6	—	—	—
Tetrabromophenolphthalein	2.0×10^6	—	3.2×10^8	—	—	—

thought to have quinone or ketone-like structures. The resistivities of these polymers ranged from 10^2 to 10^4 ohm-cm in the case of large fused ring compounds. A more typical benzophenone-terephthaloyl chloride condensation product had a resistivity of 6×10^8 ohm-cm. A possible structure is shown in Figure 7-16.

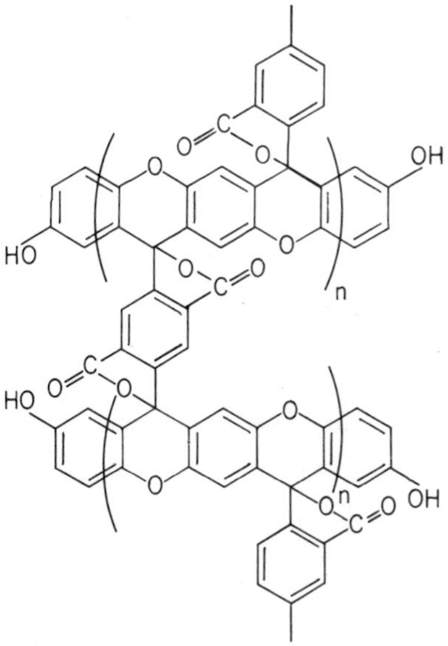

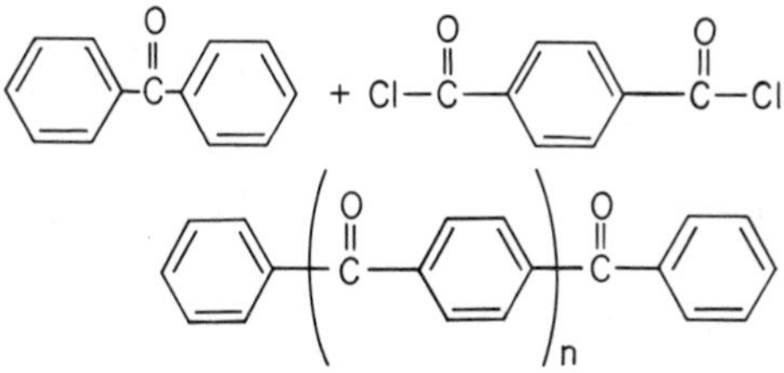

Figure 7-16. Preparation of phenylene ketone polymers.

Ferrocene ketone polymers have been prepared by Itoh.[48] A suggested structure is shown in Figure 8-17. Resistivities of such polymers ranged from 10^3 to 10^{12} ohm-cm. A similar ferrocene ketone polymer has also been sythesized by Mette and Wenger.[50] The resistivity varied from 10^6 to 10^{13} ohm-cm depending on their molecular weights.

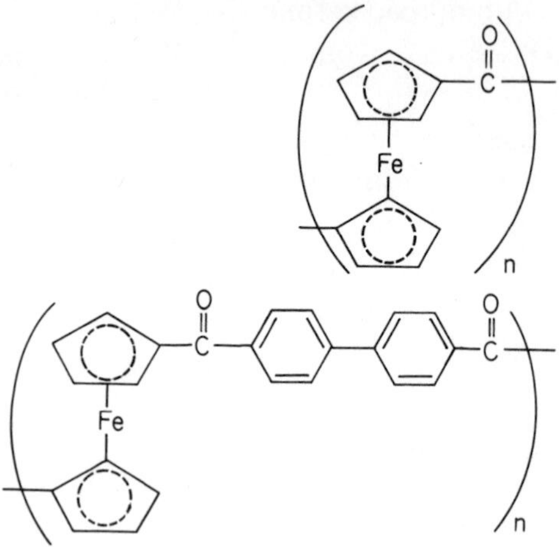

Figure 7-17. Polyferrocene ketone polymers.

Syntheses Involving Chelate Compounds

The unusual properties of phthalocyanines have long been of interest in various fields of chemistry. The electrical conductivity properties of phthalocyanine compounds were first experimentally investigated by Vartanyan[51] and then Eley.[52] They established that the conductivity of several phthalocyanine compounds varied inversely with temperature and stated that the phthalocyanines behaved similar to intrinsic semiconductors. Other conductivity studies by Kleitman,[53] Many,[54] and Felmayer[55] have essentially confirmed these findings.

The work of Felmayer, *et al.*, is particularly interesting because of exploratory studies of polymeric phthalocyanines. Polymeric phthalocyanines were obtained by the reaction of pyromellitic anhydride with molten urea. Electronic properties of polymeric phthaloyanines are compared with those of the various established phthalocyanines in Table 7-6.

Epstein and Wildi have carried out considerable work on the preparation of polymeric phthalocyanines.[56] A preferred synthesis is shown in Figure 7-18. Pyromelletic tetranitrile was obtained from pyromelletic dianhydride via pyromellitamide which was treated with phosgene in dimethylformamide. The pyromellitonitrile was condensed with cuprous chloride and urea at 300°C to

Table 7-6. Electronic Properties of Phthalocyanines.[55]

Compound	E eV*	σ_0 ohm^{-1} cm^{-1} × 10^{-3}
Copper phthalocyanine	1.79	3.82
Platinum phthalocyanine	1.52	0.229
Chlorin copper phthalocyanine	1.86	35.0
Lower polymer[a] (350°C)[b]	0.95	0.10
Higher polymer[a] (250°C)[b]	0.81	0.063

* E was calculated by using the equation $\sigma = \sigma_0 e^{-\epsilon/2kT}$.
[a] Poly-copper phthalocyanine
[b] Condensation temperature

350°C in a nitrogen atmosphere. The dried product was extracted with boiling pyridine in a Soxhlet extractor to remove traces of copper salt.

The polymeric phthalocyanines are described as "black-purple solids only slightly soluble in sulfuric acid." Molecular weights were not determined. Electronic properties were obtained on compressed (pressures greater than 20,000 psi) powder samples.

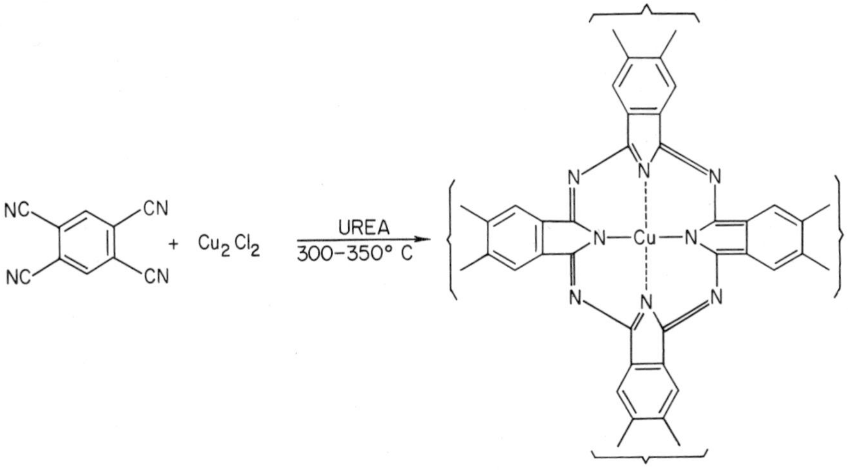

Figure 7-18. Preparation of polymeric phthalocyanines.

The experimental data showed the polymeric products to be p-type semiconductors. The activation energy and resistivity were determined to be 0.26 eV and 10^{14} to 10^{16} ohm-cm, respectively. Hall coefficients were found to depend on the oxygen pressure as shown in Table 7-7. This may be related to physical adsorption-

Table 7-7. Effect of Hall Coefficient
on Oxygen Pressure.

P_{Oxygen} (in mm of Hg)	Hall Coefficient (cc/coulomb)
0[a]	−252
209	−103
414	−39
490	0
775	+105

[a] Sample was initially evacuated to a pressure 10^{-5} mm Hg for a period of 42 hours at 23°C, constant temperature was maintained.

desorption processes roughly analogous to impurity concepts normally associated with inorganic semiconductors.

Berlin and co-workers[57] have prepared polymeric chelates from tetracyanoethylene by reaction of this compound with various metals or their compounds at temperatures up to 300°C. (See Figure 7-19.) Mixtures of tetracyanoethylene with phthalonitrile

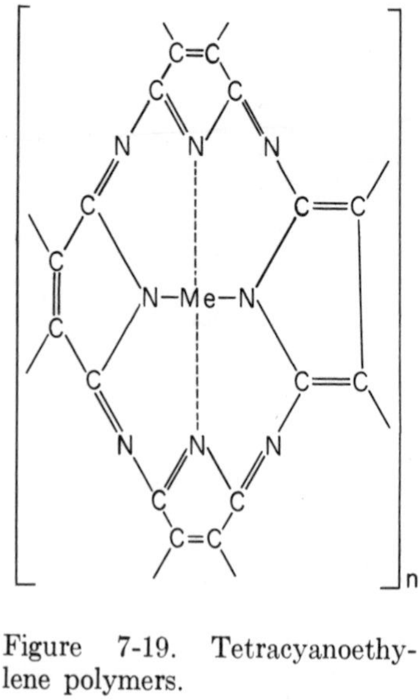

Figure 7-19. Tetracyanoethylene polymers.

were also investigated. (See Figure 7-20.) The resistivities were quite low, 10^1 to 10^2 ohm-cm with energy gaps of 0.42 to 0.52 eV.

Beryllium chelate polymers have been prepared by Underwood, et al.[58] Their electronic properties have not been determined. A suggested structure is shown in Figure 7-21.

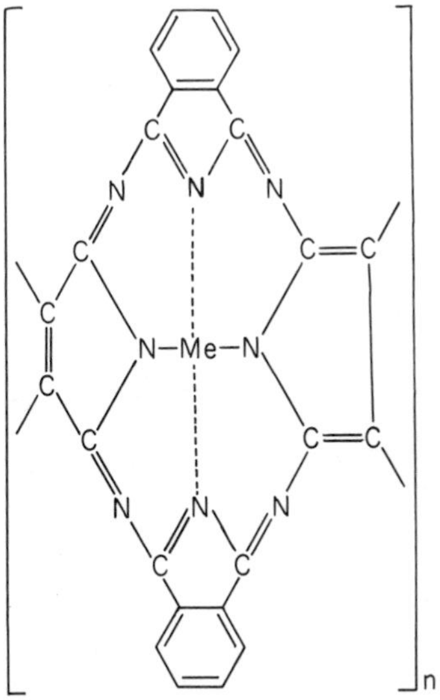

Figure 7-20. Mixtures of tetra-cyanoethylene and phthaloni-trile polymers.

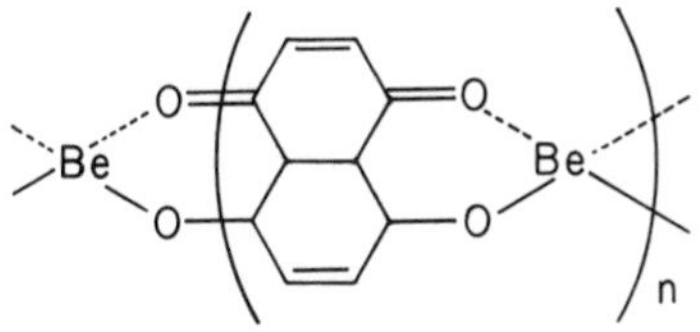

Figure 7-21. Beryllium chelate polymer.

Korshak and co-workers[59] have synthesized other somewhat similar types of chelate polymers as shown in Figure 7-22. Electronic properties are not known. Many other similar polymers can undoubtedly be synthesized.

Kanda, et al.,[60,61] have prepared polymeric chelates of 1,6-dihydroxyphenazinate and 2,5-dihydroxyquinonate. The resistivity of these chelates is as shown in Figure 7-23.

Imoto and co-workers[62] have prepared infusible black chelate polymers by the condensation of 4,5-dichlorocyclohexene-1-dione-

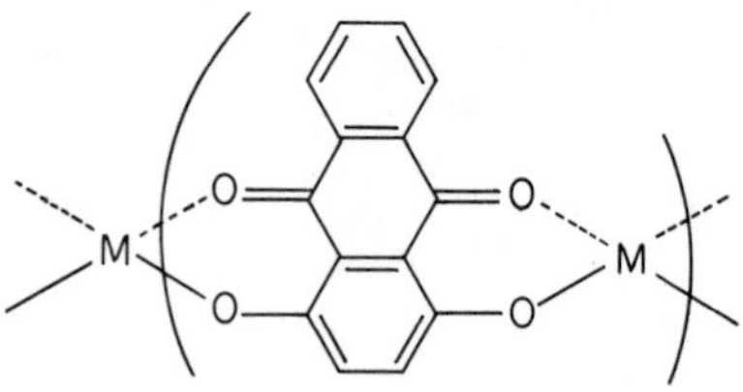

Figure 7-22. 1,4-Dihydroxyanthraqui-none chelate polymers.

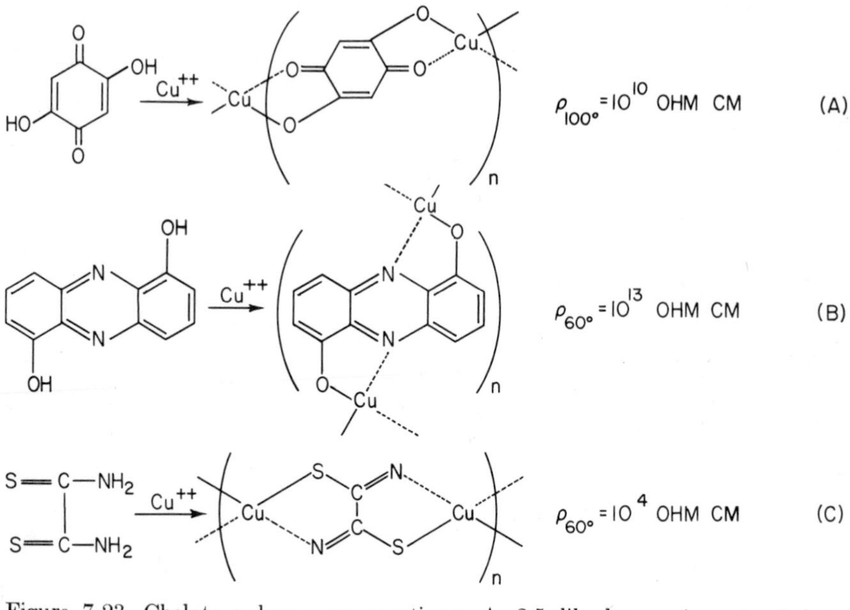

Figure 7-23. Chelate polymer preparations: A. 2,5-dihydroxyquinonate chelate polymer, B. 1,6-dihydroxyphenainate chelate polymer, C. dithioöxamide chelate polymer.

3,6 with ammonia. The electrical resistivities of several metal chelate polymers are summarized in Table 7-8.

The electrical conductivity of the polymers was found to increase with the increase in the ionization tendency of the metal ions and

Table 7-8. Electrical Resistivities of Metal
Chelate Polymer—Effect of Metal Ion.

Metal ion	Resistivity, ohm-cm
Cu^{++}	4.1×10^{10}
Pd^{++}	5.6×10^{9}
Sn^{++}	8.4×10^{6}
Zn^{++}	6.2×10^{6}
Pb^{++}	5.0×10^{11}
Hg^{++}	8.9×10^{11}
Cr^{++}	1.8×10^{10}
Co^{++}	3.5×10^{12}
Fe^{+++}	1.3×10^{12}
Sn^{++++}	3.0×10^{10}
Mg^{++}	1.3×10^{12}

their changes depended more strongly on the sort of metal ions than on sorts of ligands (see Figure 7-24).

Berlin, et al.,[63] have prepared polymeric tetrasalicyl ferrocene

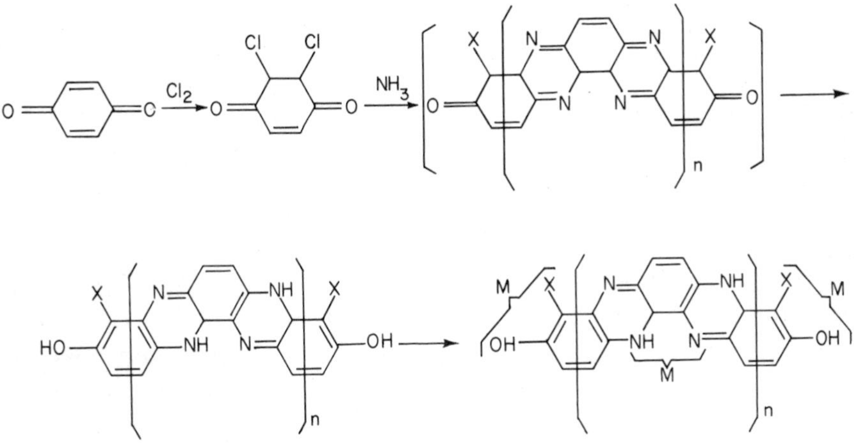

Figure 7-24. Polycondensation of benzopyrazines and formation of metal chelates. X: Cl or NH_2. M: metal ions.

chelates with Fe^{++} and Be^{++}. A suggested structure is shown in Figure 7-25. A resistivity in the order of 10^8 ohm-cm was obtained.

Amborski has recently published very interesting results in which the electrical properties of polyethylene glycol terephthalate are related to their physical structure, i.e., degree of molecular weight or crystallinity.[69] It was shown that more crystalline films of this polymer have electrical resistances one or two magnitude higher than that of the corresponding amorphous materials. Crystallization also results in a decrease of the activation energy, beside reducing the absolute level of conductivity. The conductivity decreases linearly with the polymer density as shown in Figure 7-26. A film which is about 40 per cent crystalline (density 1.375 g/cm³) has a conductivity one order of magnitude less than a

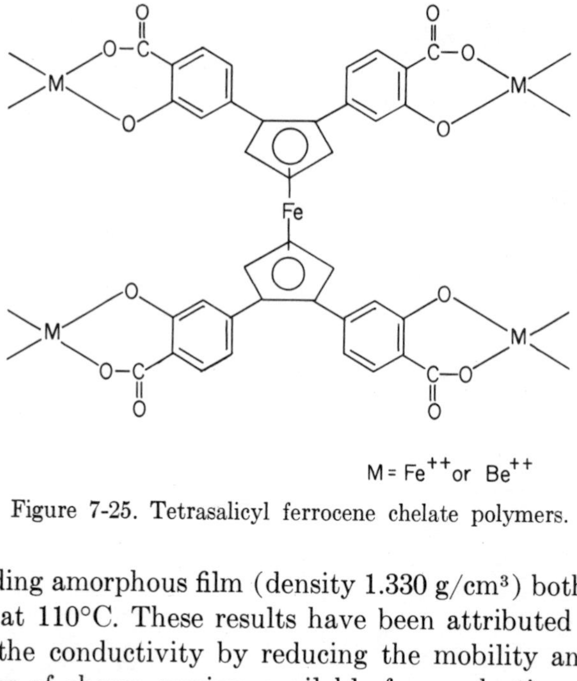

$M = Fe^{++} or Be^{++}$

Figure 7-25. Tetrasalicyl ferrocene chelate polymers.

corresponding amorphous film (density 1.330 g/cm³) both specimen measured at 110°C. These results have been attributed to the decrease in the conductivity by reducing the mobility and possibly the number of charge carriers available for conduction upon crystallization and orientation.

Ambroski also found that polyesters prepared from glycols of more than two carbon atoms have lower resistinities than the ethyleneglycol polyester. These results are shown in Figure 7-27.

Also increasing carbon chain between the phenyl groups reduces the crystallinity. Thus, a greater mobility and a decrease in resistivity would be expected. The mechanism of electronic conduc-

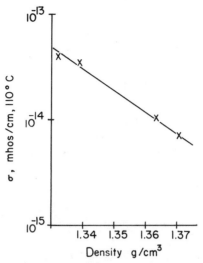

Figure 7-26. Dependence of conductivity on crystallinity.

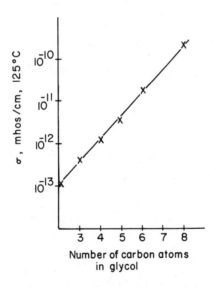

Figure 7-27. Dependence of conductivity of glycol terephthalate polyesters on glycol chain length.

tion in these polymers is, however, little understood as yet, although an ionic conduction process is favored. Further investigations of the electronic properties of these and other polymers will be necessary to better clarify the nature of the conduction processes and their structural dependence.

Miscellaneous. Measurements of the electrical properties of various nonconjugated polymeric materials including nylon, rayon, and cellophane have been reported in the literature. The magnitude of their electronic conductivities classifies them generally as nonconductors of electricity.[64,65] It has been reported that the electrical properties of polymeric materials depend on structural features associated with the type and degree of molecular order, as well as on their chemical compositions.[66,67,68]

References

1. Ellis, C., "Chemistry of Petroleum Derivatives," p. 194, New York, Reinhold, 1934.
2. Natta, G., Mazzanti, G., Corradini, P., *Rend. Accad. Maz. Lincel.*, **8**, 25, 108 (1958). Natta, G., Pino, P., and Mazzanti, G., Belgian Patents 546,151 (1956) and 548,927 (1956).
3. Luttinger, L. B., *Chem. and Ind.*, 1135 (1960).
4. Green, M. L. H., Nehme, M., and Wilkinson, G., *Chem. and Ind.*, 1136 (1960).
5. Hatano, M., Kambara, S., and Okamoto, S., *J. Poly. Sci.*, **51**, 156, 526 (1961).
6. Watson, W. H., Jr., McMordie, W. C., Jr., and Lands, L. G., *J. Poly. Sci.*, **55**, 137 (1961).
7. Korshak, V. V., Polyakova, A. M., and Suchkova, D. M., *Vysokomol. Soeden.*, **2**, 1246 (1960).
8. Berlin, A. A., Blumenfeld, L. A., Tscherkachin, M. I., Calmanson, A. F., and Selskaija, O. G., *ibid.*, **1**, 1361 (1959). Berlin, A. A., *Chim. i. Technol. Polym.*, Nos. 7–8, 1939 (1960).
9. Champetier, G., and Martynoff, M., *Compt. rend.*, **252**, 633 (1961).
10. Okamoto, A., Gordon, A., Movsovicius, F., Hellman, H., and Brenner, W., *Chem. and Ind.* 2004, (1961).
11. Stille, J. K., and Frey, D. A., *J. Am. Chem. Soc.*, **83**, 1697 (1961).
12. Tabata, Y., Sobue, H., and Hara, A., *Kogyo Kagaku Zasshi (Japan)*, **65**, 735 (1962).
13. Nehan, J. E., U.S. Patent 2,598,811.
14. Kettle, S. F. A., and Orgel, L. E., *Proc. Chem. Soc.*, 307 (1959).
15. Cairns, T. L., *J. Am. Chem. Soc.*, **74**, 5633 (1952).
16. Toland, W., U.S. Patent 3,060,179.
17. Vosburgh, W. G., *Textile Res. J.*, **30**, 882 (1960).
18. Hantz, R. C., *Textile Res. J.*, **20**, 786 (1950).
19. Burlant, J., and Parsons, J. L., *J. Poly. Soc.*, 249 (1956).
20. "Fiber from Synthesis Polymer," Ed. by R. Hill, Holland, Elsenier, 1957.

21. Shod, W., Schurz, D., and Bezer, G., Z. Physik. Chem., 210, 35 (1959).
22. Topchiyev, A. V., Geyderikh, M. A., Danydov, B. E., Kargin, V. A., Krentsel, B. A., Kustanovich, I. M., and Polak, L. S., Doklady. Akad. Nauk. SSSR, 128, 313 (1959). Chem. and Ind., 184 (1960).
23. Brennan, W. D., Brophy, J. J., and Schonhoin, H., "Organic Semiconductors," Ed. J. J. Brophy and J. W. Buttey, New York, The Macmillan Co., 1962.
24. Geiderikh, M. A., Danydov, B. E., Krentsel, B. A., Kustanovich, I. M., Polak, L. S., Topchiyev, A. V., and Voitenko, R. M., J. Poly. Sci., 54, 621 (1961).
25. Grassie, N., "Chemistry of High Polymer Degradation Processes," New York, Interscience Publishers, 1958.
26. Sorenson, W., and Campbell, T. W., "Preparative Methods of Polymer Chemistry," p. 167, New York, Interscience Publishers, 1961.
27. Mark, H., Proc. of Symp. on the Role of Solid State Phenom. on Elec. Circuits, 8, 125 (1959).
28. Bohrer, J. J., N.Y. Acad. Sci., 5, 367 (1958).
29. Winslow, F. H., Baker, W. D., and Yager, W. A., University of Buffalo Carbon Conference, Buffalo, N.Y., 1955.
30. Winslow, F. H., Baker, W. O., and Yager, W. A., J. Am. Chem. Soc., 77, 4751 (1955).
31. Bailey, W. J., and Lao, Chien-Wei, J. Am. Chem. Soc., 77, 992 (1955).
32. Clar, E., Ber., 75B, 1330 (1942).
33. Okamoto, Y., and Gordon, A. F., unpublished results.
34. Hill, D. E., and Goldsmith, G. J., Phys. Rev., 98, 238 (1955).
35. Pummerer, R., and Seligsberger, L., Ber., 64, 2477 (1931).
36. Marvel, C. S., and Hartzell, G. F., J. Am. Chem. Soc., 81, 448 (1959).
37. Edwards, G. A., and Goldfinger, G., J. Poly. Sci., 16, 589, (1955).
38. Itoh, W., Thesis, M. S., Princeton University, 1960.
39. Kovacic, P., and Kyriakis, A., Tetrahedron Letter, 11, 467 (1962).
40. Akamatu, H., and Inokuchi, H., "Symposium on Electrical Conductivity in Organic Solids," Ed. by H. Kallmann and M. Silver, New York, Interscience Publishers, 1961.
41. Berlin, A. A., and Parini, V. P., Izest. Akad. Nauk. SSSR, Ser Khim., 9, 1674 (1959).
42. Berlin, A. A., Liogonskii, and Parini, V. P., Vysokomolek Soed., 2, 689 (1960).
43. Berlin, A. A., and Matneena, N. G., Vysokomolek. Soed., 2, 1643 (1960).
44. Vogel, H., and Marvel, C. S., J. Poly. Sci., 50, 511 (1961).
45. Lenz, R. W., and Handlonits, C. E., J. Org. Chem., 25, 813 (1960).
46. Vogel, H., and Marvel, C. S., J. Poly. Sci., 50, 511 (1961).
47. McNeill, R. and Weiss, D. E., "Proceeding of the Fourth Conference on Carbon," London, Pergamon Press, 1960. Australian J. Chem., 12, 643 (1959).
48. Pohl, H. A., Bornmann, J. A., and Itoh, W., "Organic Semiconductors," Ed. by J. J. Brophy and J. W. Buttrey, New York, The Macmillan Co., 1962.
49. Engelhardt, E. H., M. S. Thesis, Princeton University, 1961.
50. Mette, H., and Wegner, W., Abstract at American Physical Society Meeting, Washington, D.C., April, 1961.

51. Vartanyan, A. T., *Zhur. Fiz. Khim.*, **22,** 769 (1948).
52. Eley, D. D., *Nature*, **162**, 819 (1948).
53. Kleitman, D., Electrical Properties of Phthalocyanine, U.S. Dept. of Commerce, Office Technical Services Report, P.B. 111419 (1953).
54. Many, A., Harnik, E., and Gehrlich, D., *J. Chem. Phys.*, **23,** 1733 (1953).
55. Felmayer, W., and Wolf, I., *J. Electrochem. Soc.*, **105,** 141 (1958).
56. Epstein, A., and Wildi, B. S., *J. Chem. Phys.*, **32,** 342 (1960).
57. Berlin, A. A., Natneeva, N. G., Sherle, A. I., *Izv. Akad. Nauk. SSSR,* **12,** 13 (1959).
58. Underwood, A. L., Toribara, T. Y., Neuman, W. F., *J. Am. Chem. Soc.,* **72,** 5597 (1950).
59. Korshak, V. V., Vinogradova, S. V., and Artemova, V. S. *Visokomol. Soed.,* **2,** 498 (1960).
60. Kanda, S., and Kawaguchi, S., *J. Chem. Phys.*, **34,** 1070 (1961).
61. Kanda, S., and Saito, Y., *Bull. Chem. Soc. Japan*, **30,** 192 (1957).
62. Inoue, H., Fuki, S., Adachi, M., and Imoto, E., *Kogyo Kagaku Zasshi*, (Japan) **63,** 2007 (1960).
63. Berlin, A. A., and Kostroma, T. V., cf. E. I. Balabanov, A. A. Berlin, V. P. Parini, V. L. Tal'roze, E. L. Frankenick and M. I. Cherkashim, *Doklady. Akad. Nauk. SSSR,* **134,** 5, 1123 (1960).
64. Hearle, J. W. S., *J. Textile Inst.*, **43,** 194 (1952).
65. Hearle, J. W. S., *J. Textile Inst.*, **44,** T177 (1953).
66. Baker, W. O., and Yager, W. A., *J. Am. Chem. Soc.*, **64,** 2171 (1942).
67. Fuoss, R. M., *J. Am. Chem. Soc.*, **61,** 2329 (1939).
68. Seitz, F., "Modern Theory of Solids," New York, McGraw-Hill, 1940.
69. Amborski, L. E., *J. Poly. Sci.*, **62,** 331 (1962).

8

Biological Systems

It has become increasingly recognized in the past decade that electron transfer processes play a most important and as yet far from fully understood role in biological processes. Szent-Györgyi suggested over twenty years ago that certain problems can be explained by the excitation of electrons into the energy band of compounds of biological interest leading to possible electron transfer between adjacent molecules.[1] The fibrous protein molecules could join together to form a medium through which an exited electron could travel. It was also suggested that such a system could hold together the insoluble oxidation enzymes of cells. The work of Baxter and Cassie on the conductivity characteristics of the wool-water and other systems brought forth the theory that the energy band for conduction was associated with the adsorbed water on the system.[2]

Eley's investigations on the semiconductivity of phthalocyanines and other organic molecules related to biologically active substances significantly carried forward the concept of semiconductivity in biological systems.[3] Of partial interest has been the idea that π orbitals overlap between the molecules to give energy bands common to the whole crystal.[4]

Today there is substantial well documented evidence that a wide range of molecules of biological interest exhibit semiconductivity in the dry crystalline or amorphous states. An excellent review has recently been prepared by Eley.[4] In this chapter electrical conductivity relationships of molecules of biological interest will be discussed.

Proteins

Many different systems of biological interest have been both qualitatively and quantitatively studied. The proteins are of particular interest for obvious reasons. One early study by Baxter and Cassie on the wool-water system's conductivities indicated that Ohm's law was obeyed.[2] The activation energy was determined as 0.7 eV. Similar results were obtained on the wool-methyl alcohol system. Baxter also measured the energy gaps of the fibrous protein collagen and also wool and silk. Values in the order of 1.3 eV were obtained. The energy gap of dried wool in a dry nitrogen atmosphere was found to be somewhat lower, i.e., 1.1 eV.[5]

Table 8-1. Electrical Conductivities of Hemoglobin and Some Amino Acids.

Substance	Resistivity ρ ohm-cm 27°C	Energy Gap, eV	
Hemoglobin	4.6×10^{12}	1.4	
Globin	4.5×10^{13}	1.5	
Ferrihaem	1.3×10^{12}	0.9	
α-alanine	5.3×10^{14}	1.7	
β-alanine	5.3×10^{12}	2.1	measured on single
Glycine	1.8×10^{13}	1.4	crystals parallel to
Glycine	1.7×10^{12}	1.5	ac plane
Diketopiprazine	1.3×10^{16}	1.1	
Oxamide	2.7×10^{15}	0.9	
Tyrosin	1.0×10^{15}	1.1	
Thymus nucleoprotein	6.2×10^{11}	1.3	
Thrombin	2.6×10^{11}	1.3	
Cytochrome C	3.8×10^{11}	1.3	
Lysozyme	3.9×10^{11}	1.3	
Fibrenogen	6.2×10^{11}	1.3	
Bovine plasma albumin	7.9×10^{11}	1.4	
Tobacco mosaic virus	1.1×10^{13}	1.5	
Elastin	2.0×10^{14}	1.5	
Collagen	2.9×10^{13}	1.4	
Gelatin	4.7×10^{13}	1.5	
Poly-ℓ-tyrosine	1.6×10^{12}	1.5	helical form ran-
Poly-ℓ-tyrosine	4.7×10^{12}	1.5	dom coil form

Eley and his co-workers studied the semiconductivity of the globular proteins, plasma, albumen, fibrinogen and edestin in the dry state and under nitrogen atmosphere. The respective energy gaps were 1.1, 1.4 and 1.3 eV. Lower values were obtained for moist materials.[6] Additional measurements with an improved experimental technique in a high vacuum on very carefully dried hemoglobin and certain amino acids.[7,8] Typical data are summarized in Table 8-1.

These electrical conductivity data are apparently quite reproducible. The energy gaps of the above noted substances are relatively high (1.0 to 2.0 eV) with charge carrier mobilities ranging

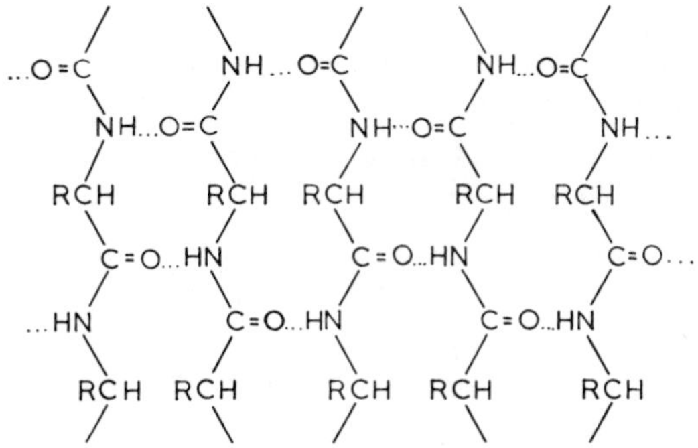

Figure 8-1. The hydrogen band in a beta-protein.

from 10^3 to 10^5 cm^2 V^{-1} sec^{-1}. It is believed that intrinsic conductivity is involved which is associated with the electron mobility of the C=O···H—N band system (Figure 8-1).

The values of the energy gaps obtained in these experiments with dry proteins are similar to the theoretical calculations of Evans and Gergely for the excitation of π electrons in the hydrogen bond systems.[9] The crystal structure of glycine is such that the nitrogen is tetrahedral and can take part in the formation of four NH···O=C bonds and in single crystals of glycine the conductivity is greater parallel the perpendicular to the planes of the hydrogen band. In oxamide structures, sheets of molecules are formed by two NH···O=C bonds of lengths 2.941 A and 2.949 A with Van der Waal's forces acting to hold them together; the nitrogen is trigonal planar.[10] The calculations of Evans and Gergely demonstrate the dependence of the energy gap on the stereochemistry of the peptide linkage. Taylor has pointed out that the electrical conduction in dry or nearly dry proteins is not yet proven to occur via mobile electrons. He considers these conduction phenomenae to be explainable on the basis of ionic or electronic conduction.[11] Therefore, further measurement of the conductivity of single peptide crystals combined with precise crystallographic data will be necessary to develop more definite conclusions on the mechanism of the conductivity.

The resistivity and energy gap of dry proteins can be changed considerably by the addition of a limited amount of an electron acceptor. When even a small quantity of chloranil is added to such a protein, the conductivity is raised significantly—by as much as 10^6.[12] This result has been explained in terms of the acceptance of electrons by the chloranil from the protein leaving positive holes in the latter's conductivity band (p-type). The addition of water further lowers the resistivity of the protein-chloranil complex by a factor of 10. Water is an electron donor and lowers the resistivity by neutralizing the positive holes. Chloranil forms similarly higher electrically conductive complexes with phthalocyanines.[13]

Addition of water to dry proteins was also found to result in a marked increase of their conductivities. Eley and Spivey observed, however, that the conductivity of hemoglobin reaches a constant value at water contents above the Brunauer-Emmett-Teller monolayer. They suggested that the water molecules are positioned on special sites and donate electrons into the conduction band of the protein molecules, thus creating an n-type conduction.[14] Additional investigations may relate conductivity changes with electron transport processes and certain phenomenae in living cells including carcinogenesis.

β-carotene

β-carotene, a C_{40} carotenoid pigment with a hydrocarbon composition and a conjugated structure, is found in both plants and animals (Figure 8-2). It is believed to take part in photosynthesis and phototropism processes and can be considered a precursor of retine, the C_{20} carotenoid pigment which is involved in all visual receptor processes.[15] Rosenberg has carried out experimental investigations of the electronic conductivity of β-carotene.[16,17] He reported that the conductivity of β-carotene obeys the usual semiconductivity relationships and determined the activation energy on compressed powder samples to be 1.5 eV for the *trans* isomer. Melted or evaporated films measured under a dry nitrogen or argon also gave the same value for the activation energy. In later studies, however, the activation energies of *trans*- and *cis*-carotene were redetermined to be 0.75 to 0.85 eV.[18] Rosenberg be-

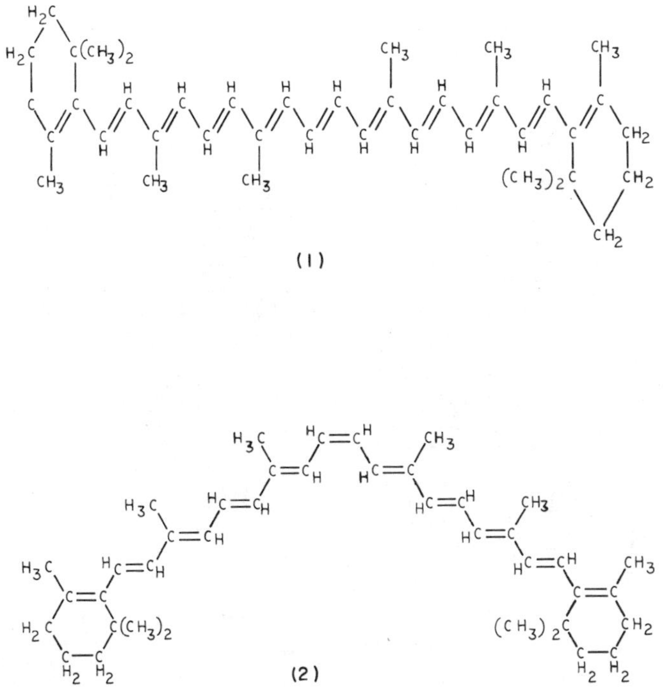

(1)

(2)

Figure 8-2. Structure of β-carotene: (1) all *trans* form; (2) 15,15 *cis* form.

lieves that these lower values are due to surface conduction phenomenae. The presence of adsorbed oxygen was also found to greatly affect β-carotene properties. Weakly adsorbed oxygen gas lowered the energy gap by 0.3 eV and raised the dark conduction 1.1×10^3 times at 25°C.[19]

Nucleic acid

Deoxyribonucleic acid (DNA) is considered to have a structure of two intertwined helical long chain molecules built up of repeating phosphate-ribose base units (Figure 8-3).[20] The bases point toward the middle of the spiral and are paired by the hydrogen bonds that build up the horizontal steps. These bonds have the structure of N—H····O=C (Figure 8-4). As each base contains 10 π electrons, each base pair has 20 π electrons. The interplanar spacing of the base pairs of 3.4 A is close to that found in graphite.

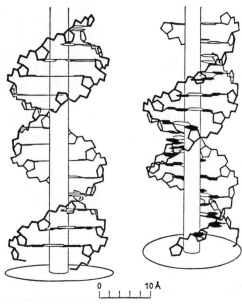

0   10 A

Figure 8-3. The double helix of DNA. (Reproduced from F. H. C. Crick and J. D. Watson, *Proc. Roy. Soc.*, **227**, 80, 1954.)

This structure suggests that it should exhibit significant conductance. Eley and Spivey measured a specific resistivity of 5×10^{11} ohm-cm at 27°C and determined the energy gap as 1.2 eV. Duchesne and co-workers reported the energy gap as 0.90 eV for a sample which may have contained a small amount of adsorbed water.[22]

Porphyrins and Dipyrromethenes

The porphyrins are closely related structurally to the phthalocyanine compounds and are of great importance in enzymes and respiratory pigments. The dipyrromethenes are also similar differing structurally mainly in stereochemistry. Phthalcyanines have been shown to exhibit significant conductivities which have been explained to be due to the π electrons present in the conjugated double bonds. The nature of the metal present in a phthalocyanine structure has apparently little effect on the conductivity and energy gap (see Chapter 4). Typical compound formulas and their structures are shown in Figure 8-5.

Some measurements have been carried out to determine conductivities of porphyrins and complex structures derived from dipyr-

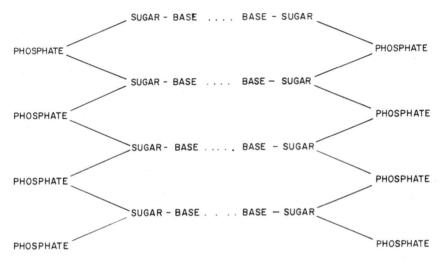

Figure 8-4. Chemical structure of DNA. The dots (. . . .) represent a hydrogen bond.

romethane.[23] These are summarized in Table 8-2. The energy gap of the typical metalloporphyrin ferrihaem, a haematin, has been determined as 1.0 eV.[7] Measured energy gaps are apparently rarely if at all affected by the nature of the central metal atom and are all in the range of 0.9 to 1.0 eV. The same was found to hold true for the complex dipyrromethane metal complexes with their somewhat different stereochemistry. Eley and Spivey found that, if bromine was used to replace the methyl in the 5 position of dipyrromethene metal complexes, the energy gap was somewhat increased due to its electron inductive effect.

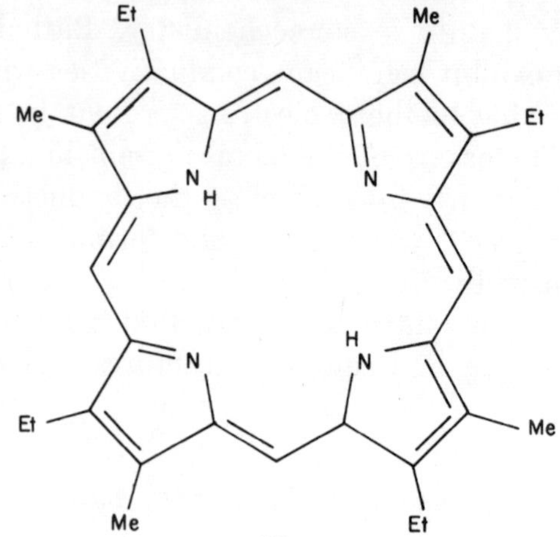

(1)
Porphyrin

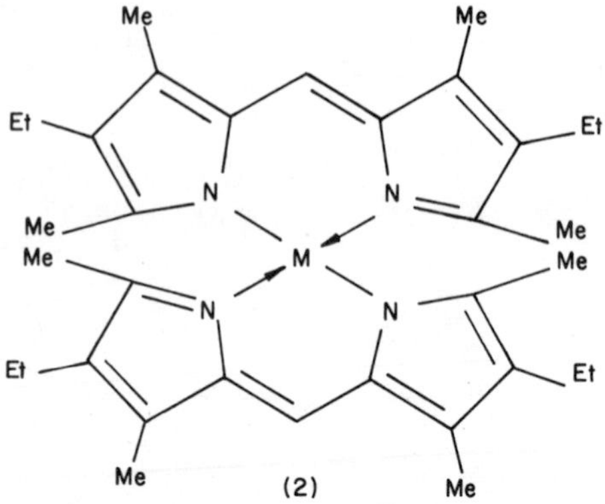

(2)
Dipyromethene metal complex

Figure 8-5. (1) Porphyrin structure; (2) dipyromethene metal complex.

Chlorophyll

Photosynthesis is considered to require that a multitude of chlorophyll molecules (Figure 8-5) function essentially as a single unit and absorb, at some locations, the four energy quanta necessary for the reduction of carbon dioxide.[24] This would suggest that excited electrons can move quite freely through the entire structure of chlorophyll molecules. A considerable amount of work is in progress to help elucidate the mechanisms involved.

Table 8-2. Electrical Properties of Porphyrins
and Dipyrromethane.

Substance	Energy Gap, E	Resistivity ρ, ohm-cm, at 27°C
Etioporphyrin	1.0	3.3×10^{13}
Co-etioporphyrin	0.95	1.7×10^{11}
Cu-etioporphyrin	0.90	3.5×10^{11}
Ni-etioporphyrin	0.90	7.8×10^{11}
Mg-etioporphyrin	0.95	1.5×10^{13}
Co-dipyrromethene[a]	0.95	1.4×10^{11}
Cu-dipyrromethene[a]	0.90	1.0×10^{10}
Co-dipyrromethene[b]	1.2	2.5×10^{11}
Cu-dipyrromethene[b]	1.2	2.8×10^{11}
Ni-dipyrromethene[b]	1.2	4.5×10^{11}

[a] 4,4'-diethyl-3,3'5,5'-tetramethyl dipyrromethane.
[b] 5-bromo-3,4'diethyl-4,3'5'-trimethyl dipyrromethene.

Katz[25] and Bradley and Calvin[26,27] have proposed the possible functioning of chloroplasts as semiconductors. Absorption of light could produce electrons and positive holes in chlorophyll. If sandwiched between a p-type and an n-type layer of lipids or lipoproteins, the electrons and holes could diffuse in opposite directions to commence the chemical oxidation and reduction cycles.

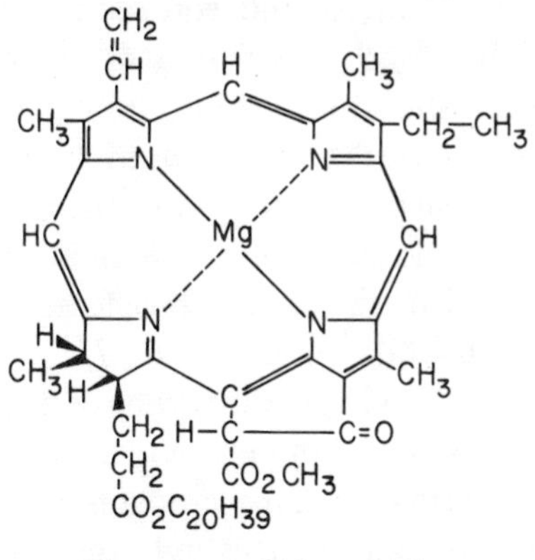

Figure 8-6. Chlorophyll a.

The first published evidence of the photoconductivity of chlorophyll was obtained by Nelson who showed that the action spectrum of its photoconduction was similar to its optical absorption spectrum.[28] This concept has been verified and extended by Terenin, *et al.*[29] and also Rosenberg and Camiscoli.[30] The latter investigations also found that the energy gaps of crystalline chlorophylls a and b measured under inert gases such as nitrogen and argon were 0.55 and 0.72, eV respectively.

Oxygen can apparently be adsorbed on the surface of chlorophyll crystals. An oxygen chlorophyll complex is formed leading to an increase in both the dark and the photocurrents. There are, however, no detectable effects of oxygen on the activation energy since the gain in current magnitude is quite small (4–10 factor).

Carcinogenesis

Cancer has been defined as an abnormal mass of tissue, the growth of which exceeds and is uncoordinated with that of the normal tissue and persists in the same excessive manner after the cessation of the stimuli which evoked the change.[31] Electrical conductivity may play a part in at least chemical carcinogenesis. Research in this field has been concerned with the studies of the relative carcinogenic activity of various biologically active compounds and also the problem of protein binding of carcinogens.[32] Binding of chemical carcinogens to tissue protein is held obligatory for the initiation of cancer. The carcinogenic activity of many aromatic hydrocarbons and related compounds is well known and amply documented by solid experimental evidence. Pullman has attempted to explain the relative carcinogenic activity of polyaromatic compounds in terms of the high electron density in the K region of the hydrocarbons, etc.[33] According to those investigators, the existence of carcinogenic activity in aromatic hydrocarbons could be correlated with the characteristics of different specific regions in the molecules known as the K, L, M regions.

The isolation of 2-phenyl-phenanthrene 3,2-dicarboxylic acid is considered to be the first experimental verification of the Pullman's concept of the interaction of a carcinogen with the constituents at the K region.[34] The binding through the K region is believed to involve an addition reaction and may be subject to steric hindrance. Also, when one K region is blocked, there is a possibility of binding to the second K region.

The formation of charge transfer complexes between a carcinogen such as a polyaromatic hydrocarbon and tissue protein has been postulated by Mason as a first step in the chemical initiation of cancer.[34,35,36] The hydrocarbons would act as electron acceptors with respect to the protein molecules. This type of electron transfer has been experimentally found to occur between proteins and strong electron acceptors, such as chloranil, but has not been verified for weak acceptors, such as hydrocarbons. The use of the conductivity method for the test of Mason's theories has been suggested.[37] Also, electron transfer from DNA to a carcinogenic hydrocarbon has been proposed recently.[38]

Retinal Rods

Some data have been developed which make feasible photoconduction of visual pigments of photoreceptors as an intermediate step between light absorption and the generation of nerve impulses.[40,41] Rosenberg and his coworkers have studied the receptors of sharp eyes obtained from freshly slaughtered animals which were immediately stored in a dark box under refrigeration.[42] For dried preparations of rods obtained by water washing the activation energy was 1.15 eV. Samples washed with sucrose solutions had an energy gap of 1.15 eV as well. These showed photoconductivity which was attributed to the presence of water in the specimen. The action spectrum was not measured accurately, but it appeared to be similar to the optical absorption spectrum of rhodopsin. With continued exposure to light, the photoconduction lessened, which may be due to structural conversion or light adaptability.

In summary, these various investigations must be considered as quite preliminary. Much of the available supporting data are indirect or pertain to dry crystalline or amorphous systems. There exist many significant objections to a direct relation of conductivity with electron transfer phenomenae in systems of biological interest. A large and intensive experimental research effort is indicated to elucidate the electron transfer mechanism of any one of the phenomenae which have been studied thus far. This should be aided by appropriate theoretical studies and calculations.

References

1. Szent-Györgyi, A., *Nature*, **148**, 157 (1941).
2. Baxter, S., and Cassie, A. B. D., *Nature*, **148**, 408 (1941).
3. Eley, D. D., *Nature*, **162**, 819 (1948).

4. Eley, D. D., in "Horizons in Biochemistry," ed. Kasha, M. and Pullman, B., New York, Academic Press, 1962.
5. Baxter, S., *Trans. Faraday Soc.*, **34**, 207 (1943).
6. Eley, D. D., Partitt, G. D., Perry, M. J., and Taysum, D. H., *Trans. Faraday Soc.*, **49**, 79 (1953).
7. Cardew, M. H., and Eley, D. D., *Faraday Soc. Discussions*, **27**, 115 (1959).
8. Eley, D. D., and Spivey, D. I., *Trans. Faraday Soc.*, **56**, 1432 (1960).
9. Evans, M. G., and Gergely, J., *Biochem. et Biophys.*, *ACTA*, **3**, 188 (1949).
10. R. Mason, *Discussions, Faraday Soc.*, **27**, 236 (1959).
11. Taylor, P., *Discussions, Faraday Soc.*, **27**, 237 (1959).
12. Davis, K. M. C., Eley, D. D., and Snart, R. S., *Nature*, **188**, 724 (1960).
13. Tollin, G., Kearns, D. R., and Calvin, M., *J. Chem. Phys.*, **32**, 1020 (1960).
14. Eley, D. D., and Spivey, D. I., *Nature*, **188**, 725 (1960).
15. Rabinowitch, E. I., "Photosynthesis," vol. II, Part 2, New York, Interscience Publishers, Inc., 1956.
16. Rosenberg, B., *J. Chem. Phys.*, **31**, 238 (1958).
17. Rosenberg, B., *J. Chem. Phys.*, **36**, 816 (1962).
18. Rosenberg, B., *J. Chem. Phys.*, **34**, 812 (1961).
19. Rosenberg, B., in "Electrical Conductivity in Organic Solids," ed. by H. Kallmann and M. Silver, New York, Interscience Publishers, 1961.
20. Crick, F. H. C., and Watson, J. D., *Proc. Roy. Soc.*, **223**, 80 (1954).
21. Eley, D. D., and Spivey, D., *Trans. Faraday Soc.*, **58**, 411 (1962).
22. Duchesne, J., Depireux, J., Bertinchamps, A., Cornet, N., van der Kaa, J. M., *Nature*, **188**, 405 (1960).
23. Eley, D. D., and Spivey, D. I., *Trans. Faraday Soc.*, **58**, 405 (1962).
24. Brillouin, L., "Horizons in Biochemistry," ed. Kasha, M., and Pullman, B., New York, Academic Press, 1962.
25. Katz, E, in "Photosynthesis in Plants," ed. by Frank, J. and Loomis, W. E., Ames, Iowa, Iowa State College Press, 1949.
26. Bradley, D. F., and Calvin, M., *Proc. Natl. Acad. Sci. U.S.*, **41**, 563 (1955).
27. Calvin, M., *Rev. Mod. Phys.*, **31**, 147 (1959).
28. Nelson, R. C., *J. Chem. Phys.*, **27**, 864 (1957).
29. Terenin, A., Putzeiko, E., and Akimov, I. *Discussion, Faraday Soc.*, **27**, 1763 (1959).
30. Rosenberg, B., and Camiscoli, J. F., *J. Chem. Phys.*, **35**, 982 (1961).
31. Willis, A. R., "Cathology of Tumors," 3rd ed., London, Butterworth Publishers, 1960.
32. Clayson, D. B., "Chemical Carcinogenesis," Boston, Little, Brown, & Co., 1962.
33. Pullman, A., and Pullman B., *Advances in Cancer Research*, **3**, 117 (1955).
34. Oliverio, V. T., and Heidelberger, C., *Cancer Research*, **18**, 1094 (1958).
35. Mason, R., *Brit. J. Cancer*, **12**, 469 (1958).
36. Mason, R., *Nature*, **181**, 820 (1958).
37. Mason, R., *Discussion, Faraday Soc.*, **27**, 129 (1959).
38. Eley, D. D., *Discussion, Faraday Soc.*, **27**, 242 (1959).
40. Hecht, S., Shlaer, S., and Pirenne, M. H., *J. Gen. Physiol*, **25**, 819 (1942).
41. Hagins, W. A., and Jennings, *Discussions Faraday Soc.*, **27**, 190 (1959).
42. Rosenberg, R. A., Orlando, R. A., and Orlando, J. M., *Arch. Biochem. Biophys.*, **93**, 395 (1961).

9
Future Trends?

The future development of organic semiconductors is somewhat difficult to assess at this time. Undoubtedly a considerable amount of the current interest in organic semiconductors is due to the possibly mistaken hope that they in some way will penetrate current uses for inorganic semiconductor materials. It is considered much more likely that new and different applications will be found for organic semiconductors which do not necessarily parallel present uses for inorganic semiconductor materials. Even more important, the study of organic semiconductors can provide new insight into the basic structure of matter with special emphasis on biological systems vital to the very life processes.[1]

Any review of recent experimental investigations of organic semiconductors must point to the surprisingly large number of "organic" compounds which have been uncovered as possessing significant electrical conductivity.[2,3] Organic semiconductors range from poly and heterocyclic aromatic hydrocarbons and phthalocyanine-like structures to the TCNQ compounds and an increasingly large array of pyrolyzed polymers, carbons, and graphitic materials. Current research, furthermore, is emphasizing that, given the increasing ability of synthetic chemistry to tailor make molecules with whatever properties are desired, the organic storehouse offers unlimited variety of possibilities and opportunities.

The investigations of the semiconductive characteristics of or-

ganic compounds are still quite new compared to efforts relating
to the development of inorganic semiconductors which date back
to the 'thirties. The many laboratories both here and abroad who
have contributed mightily to the field of inorganic semiconductor
materials are only now becoming aware of the wide open character
of organic semiconductor science and the many intriguing possibilities of such novel materials. Considering the very significant in-
vestments which have been made to promote research and development of inorganic semiconductor materials, past and current efforts
with organic semiconductors appear small indeed.[4] In spite of the
limited scale of such work, however, the great theoretical and practical importance of organic semiconductive structures has emerged
and is now being pursued more energetically.

The field of organic semiconductors is rightfully considered an
interdisciplinary area of research which includes parts of organic,
polymer, and physical chemistry, as well as physics, biology, and
medicine. The diversity of the problems encountered and the intriguing nature of the questions posed by the study of these problems makes cooperation between workers of these different dis-
ciplines essential for the future growth of this as yet largely unexplored field.

It must be recognized that the interdisciplinary nature of the
organic semiconductor field raises a serious communications problem between researchers. The languages of the organic chemist, the
physicist, and the biologist are all different; hence, proper interpretation of experimental data is becoming increasingly difficult.
A more unified approach to the field is considered essential in order
to hasten progress and avoid unnecessary and time consuming
misunderstandings. Workers in the field of organic semiconductors
must successfully solve the increasingly acute communications
problem in order to assure further growth and fruitful understanding.

Although considerable progress has been made during the past
decade to elucidate the mechanism of electrical conduction in organic solids, research is still hampered by the lack of an adequate
theoretical basis and the availability of only a limited amount of
experimental data. More quantitative investigations with emphasis on the measurement of such electronic properties as Seebeck

Effect, Hall Constant, Electron Spin Resonance Absorption, and optical properties are deemed both necessary and desirable. Furthermore, experimental efforts should emphasize the development of experimental techniques capable of furnishing reproducible data on highly purified compounds preferably as single crystals. The preparation of new compounds and the characterization of their pertinent electronic properties is considered another important step for the further development of organic semiconductors.

Considered from yet another point of view, the current lack of an adequate theoretical explanation for observed semiconductive behavior in organic solids may, given the present state of development of the field, even be advantageous. Thus, new phenomena can be observed and recorded without recourse to considerations pertaining to their relationship to theory. The larger body of experimental data which is in this way being built up may be much more amenable to adequate theoretical treatment than the currently available but too often fragmentary information.

Research in progress on organic semiconductors encompasses many different aspects of this field. It is becoming increasingly apparent that a better understanding of the mechanism of electronic conduction in organic solids and the relation of this mechanism to the physical and chemical natures of the solids under study are more necessary for further progress than "shotgun type" investigations of specific preparations and their electronic characterization. Current research projects increasingly reflect this point of view.[4,3]

The cost of organic semiconductors is most difficult to estimate at this time. Based on available information on the preparations of various organic chemicals, it is likely that the cost will depend more on the complexity of the syntheses and the amount and type of purification required than the basic raw materials employed. Furthermore, the number of structural modifications required to introduce certain desirable end product characteristics for specific applications may become an important factor as well. In general, however, the cost of organic semiconductors produced on a volume basis should be more than competitive with that of the various inorganic materials in use today.

In addition to the above considerations, organic semiconductors may well be prepared as structures with sufficient physical strength properties to greatly facilitate the fabrication of various devices and components. Thus, molded shapes, films, fibers, etc., of organic semiconductors could be produced to make possible semiconductor component and device manufacture at greatly reduced cost. The ready availability of lower cost semiconductor components and devices could, in turn, further stimulate demand.

Organic semiconductors are rather likely to exhibit significantly lower thermal conductivities than their inorganic counterparts. For thermoelectrical semiconductor applications this probable characteristic of organic semiconductors will appreciably increase their figure of merit, thus greatly enhancing their applicability.

It has often been stated that the limited thermal stability of organic chemical compounds may become a major handicap for organic semiconductors. This point of view, however, does not take into account the excellent thermal stability of various specific types of organic structures, such as, for example, the phthalocyanines, certain fluorinated compounds, aromatic polyamides, polyesters, and, most recently, the polyimides. Indications are, moreover, that, as knowledge of synthesis and structure continues to increase, still more heat resistant structures can be expected. As a matter of fact, the heat resistance of some of the more heat stable organic compounds already exceeds the usable service temperature range of certain inorganic semiconductor compounds and alloys now in use.

Some questions have also been raised about the environmental resistance of organic semiconductor materials. Experimentally obtained data indicate that many organic compounds, especially high molecular weight materials, may possess superior chemical resistance compared with a number of widely used inorganic semiconductor materials which are apt to experience the deleterious effects of corrosion and other undesirable phenomenae when contacted by moisture, chemicals, etc.

Further research on organic semiconductors can thus take into account not only that the existence of compounds capable of significant amount of electron transport has been experimentally verified but also that such compounds may exhibit a number of potentially particularly useful characteristics for specialized application. It is in these fields that economic manufacture at levels competitive to inorganic semiconductor materials is most likely. Given this knowledge, the next decade should witness most significant growth of this still wide open field of research.

Speculation about the possible applications of organic semiconductors need be limited only by one's imagination.[2,4] Implications of organic semiconductor research range from diverse solid state phenomena and organic reaction kinetics to organic catalysis and biophysical and biochemical mechanisms and processes. Organic semiconductors may find important uses in thermoelectric converters, solid state batteries, information storage systems, sea water conversion, ion exchange resins, electroluminescent devices, electrets, and many other areas as well. A very important field of research is undoubtedly the application of semiconductivity to biochemistry and biophysics.[1]

Biological semiconductivity and its many faceted effects on many different body processes have been subject to mainly speculative but also experimental considerations ever since Szent Gyorgyi called attention to the study of energy levels in biochemistry (1941).[7] Of all the various classes of organic substance of interest to the biochemist which have shown significant semiconductivity, the so called charge transfer complexes play probably a most significant role. Phthalocyanines, porphyrines, proteins, polyamides, polyurethanes, nucleic acids, and nucleo-proteins are organic semiconductors.

Semiconduction mechanisms are being investigated in connection with cytochrome systems, chloroplasts, retinal rods, radiation effects, and carcinogenesis as well as prosthetic group-protein interactions.[1] It is possible that electron acceptors such as quinones may induce highly conducting p-type protein systems to the required low resistivity levels.

The three main known causative agents for cancer are radiation, viruses, and chemicals. The relative carcinogenic activity of polyaromatic compounds has been experimentally investigated. It has been proposed that tissue proteins donate an electron to the hydrocarbon molecule which accepts it, forming a charge transfer complex. The binding of chemical carcinogens to tissue protein is obligatory for the initiation of cancer. The implications of further research on the initiation and possibly prevention of carcinogenesis are most interesting.

The idea of electron transfer of DNA to carcinogenic hydrocarbons has also been proposed.[8,9] Charge transfer complexes could arise from radiation effects as well as from carcinogenic agents.

Certain thermally stable organic semiconductor systems are being considered for the production of thermoelectric devices. These include phthalocyanine polymers and certain pyrolyzed polymer structures. Monsanto Chemical Co. has recently been granted U.S. Patent 3,046,322[11] and 3,046,323[12] covering the preparation of pyromellitonitrile/hydrogen sulfide reaction products and their application to both thermoelectric and photoelectric devices. From thermoelectric tests samples of this organic semiconductor material showed a thermoelectric power of -24 to -56 microvolts/$°$C (n-type conductivity). Additional heat treatment produces materials with a p-type semiconductivity. This p-type semiconductivity could be maximized by optimum treating temperatures and time of treatment.

For the future, a significant expansion of such work can be anticipated. It is quite likely that commercially usable thermoelectric and photoelectric devices will be developed from suitably improved organic semiconductor systems for specialized end product applications. The current activities in this field suggest that substantially higher figures of merit will be achieved which may in fact surpass those obtainable with inorganic thermoelectric materials on account of the lower thermal conductivity of the organics.

Australian researchers have pioneered the concept of semiconductive ion exchange type resins for applications such as desalting of sea water.[10] Ions that are absorbed on the semiconductive polymer could be removed later, and the ion exchange resin be regenerated either continuously or batchwise electrically. The requirements for a suitable semiconductive ion exchange polymer sorbant include high exchange capacity, chemical stability, and an electrical conductivity approximately of the same order as that measured for sea water. As a first step towards the realization of this idea, certain modified xanthene polymers have been synthesized.

Following up this approach Pohl has proposed the use of semiconductive ion exchange resins for the processing and purification of various chemical streams.[2] These redox resins could oxidize or reduce the substrate passing through at selected potentials. They could operate continuously and reversibly and would add only a minimum of extraneous materials.

The development of novel and improved materials for memory devices appears well within the reach of organic semiconductor systems. Certain materials now under investigation exhibit a remarkable fast speed of response. Also, the low temperature mechanical strength properties of many organic semiconductor systems are of a high order.

Organic semiconductors may also find applications in the rapidly growing laser and maser fields. Laser action has recently been demonstrated with certain organic rare earth metal complexes. The employment of organic semiconductors can render feasible the development of an entirely new set of devices and compounds with unique performance characteristics.

Pyrolized organic semiconductive polymers may result in a variety of useful end products from improved chemical catalysts to electrodes with superior use properties.[2] The feasibility of preparing such electrodes is said to be demonstrable on a laboratory scale. Catalytic effects of semiconductive polymer carbons are being experimentally evaluated in a variety of chemical processes ranging from the alkylation of petroleum fractions to the polymerization of olefin monomers.

Preliminary experiments indicate that phosphors can be both modified and enhanced in their performance characteristics. Such investigations may have an important bearing on the future development of television and many other communication devices. Organic semiconductors are also of interest for the development of electronic optical shutters which, when perfected, will in turn usher in an entirely new group of devices and components.

Improved methods of reproduction for printed and photographic materials are being investigated with organic semiconductor materials. Certain experimental printing processes could be substantially improved in efficiency by the use of suitable organic semiconductors. There exist also intriguing industrial possibilities for semiconductive organic pigments.

There is, of course, the not to be neglected possibility that an organic semiconductor can be synthesized with properties comparable to those exhibited by inorganic semiconductor materials. Such a development could result in the application of organic semiconductors for transistors and the wide array of now existing derivative devices and components of the electronics industry. The large scale employment of organic semiconductor materials in the electronic field may be expected to follow swiftly the acceptance of an organic semiconductor transistor.

Organic semiconductors stand on the threshold of a bright and exciting future. The opportunities exist to solve some of the most important problems of the life processes as well as to develop a diverse and as yet far from fully realized group of novel devices, components etc., for applications ranging from printing to sea water conversion to potable water. It is up to the inquisitive and ever questioning spirit of modern science to fulfill the promise in this field.

References

1. Kasha, M., and Pullman B., "Horizons in Biochemistry," New York, Academic Press, 1962.
2. Pohl, H. A., *Chem. Eng.*, 104–110, (Oct. 30, 1961).
3. *Chem. Eng. News*, 86–96, (Feb. 26, 1962).
4. PB 18 1037 "Organic Semiconductors—Their Technological Promise," OTS Washington 25, D.C. (1962).
5. Felmayer, W., and Wolf, I., *J. Electrochem. Soc.*, **105**, 141 (1958).
6. Epstein, A., and Wilde, B. S., *J. Chem. Phys.*, **32**, 324 (1960).
7. Szent-Györgyi, A., *Nature*, **148**, 157 (1941).
8. Pullman, A., and Pullman B., *Advances in Cancer Research*, **3**, 117 (1955).
9. Oliverio, V. T., and Heidelberger C., *Cancer Research*, **18**, 1904 (1958).
10. MacNeill, R., and Weiss, D. E., Proceedings of the Fourth Conference on Carbon, p. 281, London, Pergamon Press, 1960.
11. Wildi, B. S. (to Monsanto), U.S. Patent 3,046, 322 (1962).
12. Wildi, B. S. (to Monsanto), U.S. Patent 3,046,323 (1962).

Index